CORNING

A STORY OF DISCOVERY AND REINVENTION

DAVIS DYER

Dedicated to all the employees
of Corning, who have contributed to the success
of the company and made the world
a better place to live.

First published in the United States in 2001
by Corning Incorporated, Corning, NY

Library of Congress Card Number: 00-111916

ISBN 0-9707409-0-5

Designed by
Kohn Cruikshank Inc, Boston

Printed and bound in the U.S.A.

PREFACE

When we came to Corning in the 1960s, the Glass Works (as it was then called) had long since established itself as the preeminent specialty glass company in the United States and as a technology leader worldwide. We had recently introduced Pyroceram, the glass ceramic material used in Corning Ware and missile nose cones. A pioneer in space-age materials, the company was poised on the threshold of a bright new era. That was a powerful incentive for us and a lot of other people to join the company. Corning has a distinguished past, but it is a company that has always looked forward.

Nearly four decades later, as we observe the 150th anniversary of our first ventures in making glass, we continue to push the frontiers of technology in our industry. The age of information is upon us, and Corning is poised to lead once again. This is an old theme in our history What we're doing now in photonics, new information displays, advanced life science products, and in many other frontier areas is consistent with what we've always done. From its earliest decades, Corning has found ways to engineer glass and materials to meet the practical requirements of industries that provide essential benefits to society: the railroads and transportation, electric lighting, consumer housewares, electronics and television, environmental products, and telecommunications. Our success in these industries has enabled Corning's businesses to span the globe. We have operations in over thirty countries, research centers in five, and we draw employees and new ideas from everywhere in the world.

This book describes and illustrates how we've done it. It is a story not only of research and technology but also of people who have led the company, administered its operations, and developed, manufactured, and sold its products. It is also a story of the deep interdependence between the company, its employees, and the community in which it is based. Today's employees and owners—as well as tomorrow's—owe a deep measure of gratitude to those who have brought the company this far in its continuing journey.

Roger G. Ackerman
Chairman of the Board
June 2001

John W. Loose
Chief Executive Officer

A Tradition of Specialties

1851–1880

The story of Corning Incorporated opens in Somerville, Massachusetts, in 1851, when 38-year-old Amory Houghton, an enterprising merchant, bought a stake in a small glass company called Cate & Phillips and became a director. From that moment, the fortunes of the Houghton family and the companies they founded have been tightly bound with glass. Yet the early years of this long, productive relationship were hardly promising. The glass industry and the markets it served were evolving rapidly, and it took decades, misfortunes, and struggles before the Corning Glass Works carved out an enduring place as a maker of specialty glass products.

Houghton hailed from a long line of New England farmers and merchants. He apprenticed as a carpenter and by his early 20s had his own contracting business in Cambridge, Massachusetts. He married well, to Sophronia Oakes, the daughter of a wealthy Boston merchant, and he launched several new ventures, including real estate and the trading of wood, coal, and other materials—sometimes with the assistance of his in-laws. According to family lore, Houghton made and lost several fortunes along the way. In 1851, a veteran British "gaffer" (master glassblower) named Teasdale intrigued him with the commercial possibilities of making glass—a versatile material that could be rolled into windows, blown into globes, lamp chimneys, and bottles, drawn into tubing for thermometers and scientific ware, pressed into dishes and containers, and cut into useful or ornamental objects and fine works of art.

Soon after Houghton bought in, Cate & Phillips changed its name to Bay State Glass, and evidently it fared well. By 1854, he was able to invest $60,000 to become the proprietor of another glass company in Somerville, Union Glass Works. After a fast start, however, Union Glass nearly collapsed during the panic of 1857. Still, there were hopeful signs for the future. In that same year, Houghton's 20-year-old son, Amory Jr., joined the company. The younger Houghton had apprenticed with a dealer in paints and varnishes and developed a strong interest in chemistry. At Union Glass, he set up a small laboratory to experiment with colored glass formulas and recorded his findings in a "recipe book" that was seldom out of his sight. The company soon acquired a reputation for producing glass of high quality and consistent coloring.

Outgrowing its local market, Union Glass opened a wholesale outlet in New York City. In 1864, the elder Houghton saw an opportunity to take over the struggling Brooklyn Flint Glass Works—again with help from his in-laws—and he sold his stake in Union Glass and moved south. Amory Jr. followed as well, and both men served as directors and officers of Brooklyn Flint Glass. Another son, Charles, also joined the business. Unfortunately, the Houghtons were not able to restore the

The Corning Glass Works served the dominant national industry of the era: the railroads.

Amory Houghton Jr.'s formula for copper ruby glass set the railroad industry's standard for signal glass.

company's prosperity. A fire closed the factory for several months in 1866, while glassmakers in the western states, especially Pennsylvania and Ohio, posed a serious competitive threat. The western glassmakers enjoyed lower costs and could reach eastern markets through the emerging network of railroads. At the same time, they were developing new "lime glass" formulations that proved cheaper and more workable than lead "flint glass" for popular applications such as windows, dishes, bottles, and drinking glasses. In 1867, with Brooklyn Flint Glass under siege, Sophronia Houghton assumed the company's debt while her husband and sons sought ways to save the business.

Fortunately, help arrived from an unexpected quarter. Elias Hungerford, a banker from Corning, New York, had a vision of transforming his hometown into a center of glassmaking. Situated in the Southern Tier of New York State, the town was about 250 miles northwest of New York City and was striving to emerge from the shadow of Elmira, its robust neighbor to the east. Corning was served by the Erie Railroad and the Chemung Canal, a feeder that linked the Chemung River to the Erie Canal via Seneca Lake. Ample deposits of coal and sand stood nearby, and Hungerford himself had developed an idea for a new glass product—colored window blinds—that he hoped would sell.

After the Glass Works moved to Corning in 1868, it served a thriving local industry in cut glass.

His plan hinged on luring an existing glass company to Corning, and in Amory Houghton Sr., he found a willing partner. In May 1868, the board of Brooklyn Flint Glass agreed to move its entire business to Corning in return for $50,000 in local investments—out of $125,000 in total capital. The glass-cutting firm Hoare & Dailey, which had previously shared quarters with Brooklyn Flint Glass, also agreed to move.

The Corning Flint Glass Works fired up its new factory in October 1868, with employment of about 200 men, including a handful who accompanied the Houghtons from Brooklyn. The initial products included goblets, globes, jars, fruit dishes, lamp chimneys, and glass blanks for cutters and engravers.

The optimism that accompanied the move from Brooklyn to Corning evaporated quickly, however. Local varieties of coal did not burn at even temperatures required by glass ovens, and local sand was not suitable for making high quality glass.

Nor could the Hungerford window blind be manufactured economically. These problems and relentless competition pushed the Corning Flint Glass Works into receivership in 1870. Amory Houghton Sr. left the business and spent the remainder of his days on a farm in Westchester County or his townhouse in Brooklyn.

The bankers who owned the company understood that the best hope of recouping their losses lay in the hands of Amory Houghton Jr. That hope proved well founded, and by 1872, the company had regained solvency. Assisted by his brother Charles, Houghton arranged to repurchase the factory through a loan. Within three years, they paid off the loan and incorporated the company as the Corning Glass Works, with $50,000 in capital. Its owners included the Houghton brothers, an uncle, and a key manager, Joseph Tully, whose family would soon be joined to the Houghtons by marriage. (A descendant, Alice Tully, would become, like her Houghton cousins, a major patron of the arts in New York City. Alice Tully Hall at Lincoln Center is named for her. Another famous heir of the founding group was the actress Katharine [Houghton] Hepburn, granddaughter of Alfred Houghton, younger brother of Amory Jr. and Charles.)

The rebirth of the Glass Works depended not only on the energies of the owners and employees, but also on an important shift in thinking about the company's place in the glass industry. Rather than attempt to make a broad line of glass products in which it competed at a disadvantage, the Houghtons chose instead to focus on a few specialty items, including colored glass for signal lenses, blown glass for lamp globes and chimneys, glass tubing for scientific and industrial uses, and glass blanks for cut crystal glassware. These products filled essential needs in the fast-growing American economy, and Corning proved adept at making them.

Amory Houghton Jr.'s notebooks reveal his meticulous approach to glassmaking and special interest in colored glass.

As railroad traffic boomed in the post-Civil War era, for example, reliable and durable glass for signals became essential to ensure safety. Amory Jr. continued his experiments with colored glass, developing in 1874 a superior copper ruby glass that the railroads adopted as an industry standard. Charles, meanwhile, worked on lens design, employing the services of Cornell University optical expert George S. Moler. Standard lens design called for bulls-eye corrugations on the outside of the glass to concentrate the light and extend its visibility. Such lenses tended to collect dirt and grime, and ice and snow could obscure them. Charles solved this problem by designing a lens with the corrugations on the inside. His patent for the inverted fresnel lens was Corning's first. Drawing on its own knowledge of glass chemistry and Moler's expertise, the Glass Works became the nation's leading supplier of signal glass to the railroad and marine industries.

Corning displayed similar proficiency in making other specialty glass items. The railroads consumed growing volumes of the company's lamp globes for railroad cars and stations. Manufacturers of scientific and medical apparatus prized Corning's hand-drawn glass tubes for thermometers, barometers, and druggists' and chemical ware. The company's high quality crystal glass blanks nourished a thriving local industry of glass cutters and engravers. By the turn of the century, such firms as Hoare & Dailey, Hawkes Rich Cut Glass Company, and H. P. Sinclaire & Co. enabled Corning, New York to promote itself as "the Crystal City."

In later years, of course, Corning's business changed dramatically as new product lines emerged and old ones withered and disappeared. But the company's essential character and role established in the 1870s as a maker of specialty materials with its roots in the Chemung Valley remained constant. By applying research to unlock the mysteries of glass, and by courting assiduously fast-growing and demanding customers, Corning developed a steady stream of specialty products, ranging from scientific glassware, to aircraft and spacecraft windows, to advanced optical systems.

Amory Houghton Sr. launched his family into the glass business in 1851. His wife, Sophronia Oakes Houghton, helped rescue her husband's ventures when they stumbled, and their children found a formula for enduring business success.

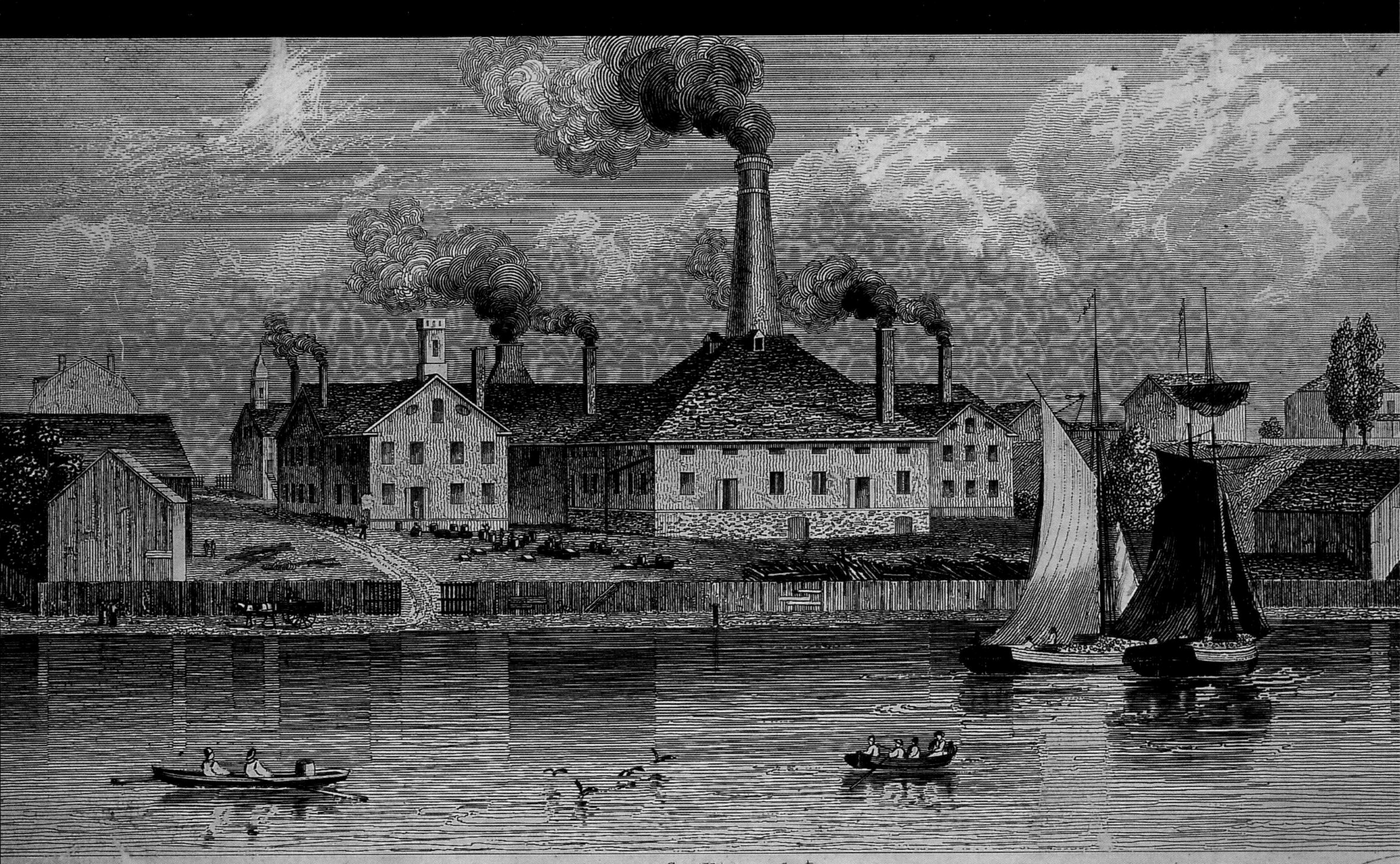

Brooklyn, N. Y., December, 1867.

Gentlemen:

The subscribers would respectfully inform you that their WORKS having been rebuilt and greatly enlarged, they are now prepared with increased facilities to furnish all kinds of

Rich Cut, Plain Blown, and Pressed Glassware,

in plain flint and colors. They are also prepared to furnish at short notice the best quality of CANE GLASS, of all sizes and colors, suitable for the MANUFACTURE OF BUTTONS, DRESS TRIMMINGS, &C.

THERMOMETER, BAROMETER, VIAL, AND GAUGE TUBING drawn to order, and warranted to give entire satisfaction.

DRUGGISTS' AND CHEMICAL GLASSWARE.

Special attention given to private MOULDS, and MOULDS made to order for parties desiring them.

Attention given to Matching odd articles both in Cut and Plain Glass.

Having had many years' experience in the Glass business, we feel confident in being able to execute orders promptly and in a manner calculated to please.

Soliciting a share of your business,

We remain, Yours, Truly,

BROOKLYN FLINT GLASS WORKS,

A. HOUGHTON, Treasurer.

In 1864, the Houghtons moved from Somerville to take over the Brooklyn Flint Glass Works, situated on the shore across from Manhattan. Founded in 1823, the company had earned international renown for its high quality blanks that were cut into fine crystal bowls, glasses, and decanters.

After a fire destroyed the factory in Brooklyn, the Houghtons rebuilt the operation and optimistically promoted a variety of wares. The company continued to struggle, however, when a new opportunity appeared in 1868.

Pictured in 1867, the year before the Glass Works arrived, Corning was already bustling and not even muddy streets could obscure its ambition.

Corning, New York banker Elias Hungerford and local boosters wooed the owners of the Brooklyn Flint Glass Works to move upstate. Hungerford believed that the company might thrive by making glass window blinds.

The product failed to spark much interest, although today (left) it remains a curiosity on display in the Corning Museum of Glass.

Inside the factory, gaffers (master glassblowers) working with young assistants produced glass objects. The gaffer in the foreground is William Woods, later the inventor of the Ribbon Machine that automated manufacture of light bulbs.

Viewed from the south, the twin chimneys of the Corning Glass Works—sited on land now occupied by the company's modern headquarters—dominate the town's skyline. Note the bucolic scenery across the Chemung River

The second generation of the founding family—Charles, Alfred, and Amory Jr. (left to right)—believed that Corning would prosper by applying scientific methods of research and production to glassmaking. Charles patented a new design for signal lenses, while Amory Jr. developed proprietary formulas for colored glass compositions. Alfred worked off and on for the Glass Works but is best remembered as the grandfather of the actress Katharine Hepburn.

Thomas Hawkes won the prestigious Grand Prize at the Paris Exhibition in 1889 for his crystal glassware—the first American firm so honored.

At an impromptu celebration in Corning, Charles Houghton, John Hoare, and other prominent citizens offered congratulations and the Fall Brook Band serenaded the crowd.

Hoare & Dailey engraved these crystal decanters to commemorate the opening at the Corning, Geneva to Syracuse Railroad in 1877.

Irishman John Hoare started a glass cutting firm in Brooklyn in 1853. He bought his blanks from Brooklyn Flint Glass and moved with that company to Corning fifteen years later. Hoare & Dailey occupied the second floor of the Glass Works factory.

Thomas G. Hawkes began working as a glass cutter at Hoare & Dailey in Brooklyn, then followed his employer to Corning. In the early 1880s, he left to start his own glass cutting business, which soon became the city's largest. Hawkes, in turn, spawned other glass businesses, including the Steuben Glass Company, and helped Corning validate its boast of being "the Crystal City."

Located at 77 West Market Street, Hawkes & Co. included a show room on the ground floor beneath cutting and engraving shops on the second and third floors.

In 1877, Charles Houghton obtained the company's first patent for a new design for signal lenses that moved the corrugations from the outside to the inside. The resulting smooth exterior made the lens more visible and easier to clean.

The Glass Works retained Cornell optics professor George S. Moler in the 1870s to advise on lens design. Thus began long-standing traditions of applying science to its products and of forming alliances with outside parties to gain specialized expertise.

Corning means **dependability** *in railroad glassware*

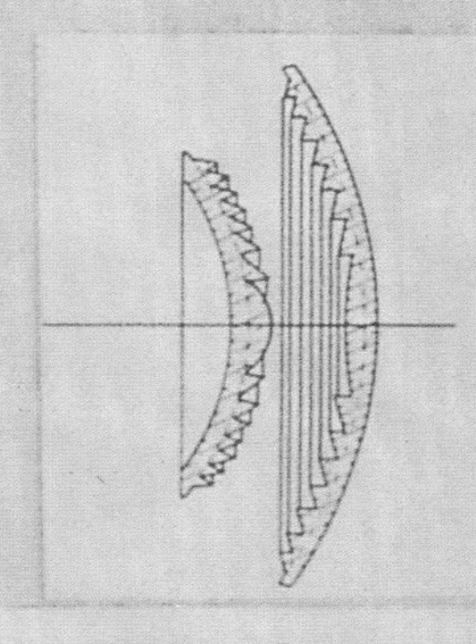

The CORNING® Doublet Lens.

One of many Corning contributions to better signals. Colored inner lens is protected—combination of two lenses gives excellent beam pattern.

Day by day, your unseen partners at Corning seek to improve the railroad lenses that, for over 50 years, have enjoyed an unchallenged reputation for dependability—adhering to rigid color specifications . . . precise optical characteristics . . . accurate dimensions . . . and durability of the glass itself.

CORNING GLASS WORKS
CORNING, N. Y.

Corning means research in Glass

Suffragette and birth control activist Margaret Sanger (pictured here standing, second from left) is one of the most famous natives of Corning, New York.

Her legacy lives on in the city, where the Planned Parenthood Center (a cause supported by Corning and many employees) is named jointly for Sanger and Katharine Houghton Hepburn (behind the baby), mother of famous actress Katharine Hepburn and another strong advocate of women's rights and birth control.

By the 1880s, the Corning Glass Works had established itself securely as a leading supplier of specialty glass items. It also proved securely profitable, and the owners and their descendants could afford to live well. Pictured: Amory Houghton Jr. enjoyed driving about town in his carriage. One of these excursions so impressed young Thomas Watson of Painted Post that he determined to make a career in business. He followed up by transforming a small company that manufactured adding machines into the International Business Machines Corporation — IBM.

Descendants of Corning Glass Works co-founder Joseph Tully, William and Clara Tully and their daughter Alice, prepare to fly across the English Channel in 1929. Alice Tully later became a leading patron of the arts, especially in New York City, where a concert hall at Lincoln Center is named in her honor.

As Corning's business expanded and diversified, specialty glass products remained a signature product line. Pictured here: scientific glassware at the company's facility on Cortlandt Street in New York City, c. 1920.

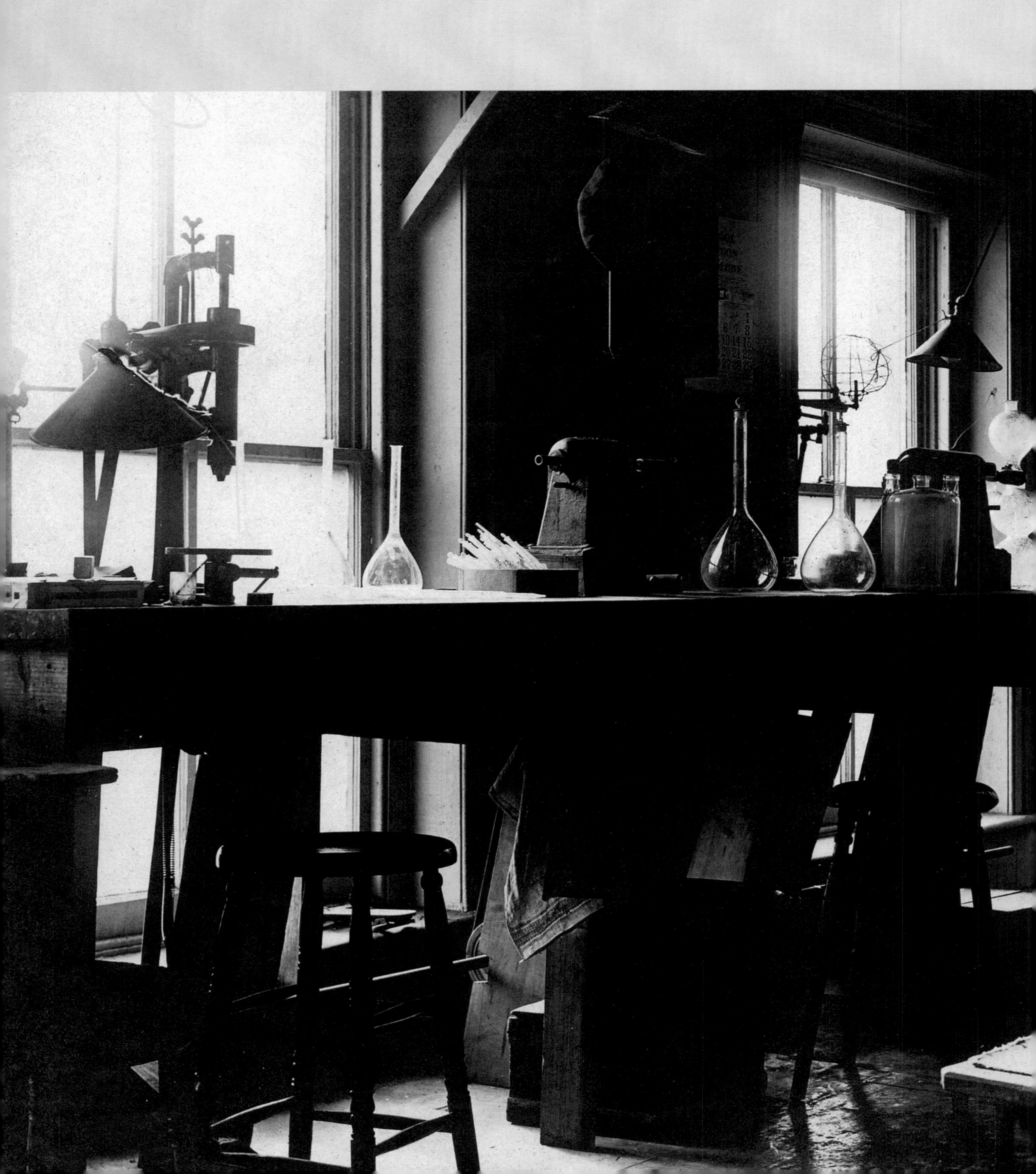

Among the company's recent specialty products are items made of high purity fused silica — the purest known form of glass.

In 1999, this high purity fused silica facility near Charleston, South Carolina, came on stream. One of the newest plants makes the company's oldest products: specialty glass for demanding applications in science and industry.

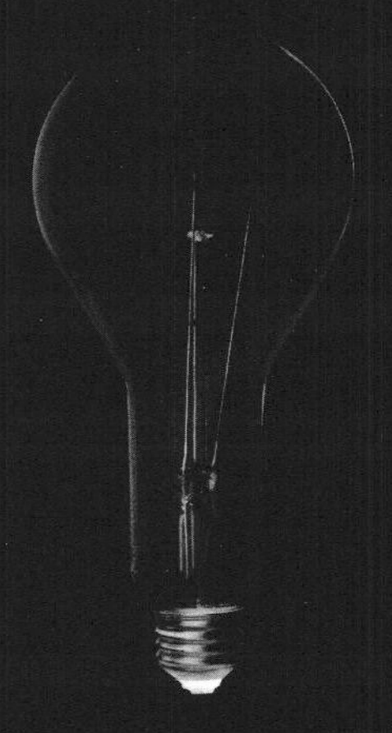

An Age of Illumination

1880-1930

In 1879, Thomas Alva Edison, a 32-year-old self-taught inventor, demonstrated to his own satisfaction an incandescent electric light. The essential ingredients were a metal filament heated by electrical current in a vacuum. In the lore of the lightbulb, this was all that mattered. Yet there was another necessary ingredient, easy to overlook, perhaps, because it was transparent: the glass envelope that held the vacuum, protected the filament, and enabled the light to radiate outward with minimal loss.

Edison realized that producing lightbulbs in high volume would require glass of a proper formulation—tougher and more resistant to heat than lime glass used in windows and jars, yet able to be formed to a standard bulb shape. He found exactly what he needed at Corning Glass Works. Edison also came to admire the skill of Corning gaffers in blowing bulbs quickly, reliably, and cheaply. In 1880, he identified the company as his sole supplier of glass tubes and bulbs.

The successful launch of the lightbulb transformed Corning's business and helped establish the company as a major factor in the electrical products industry for more than a century. Together with the railroad signal business of its initial years, the linkage to lighting formed a pattern that would recur again and again in Corning's history: a hidden but essential role in the development of major innovations and industries that improved the quality of life.

By 1889, glass for electric lamps accounted for three-quarters of Corning's total business—but still less than $1 million—and had prompted several major additions to the factory, which now boasted five tanks with chimneys. The company not only supplied Edison—whose electric lighting operations would soon be merged into the General Electric Company—but also Edison's main rival, Westinghouse, and other makers of lightbulbs.

It is sometimes assumed that electric lighting swept across the country after the invention of the electric lightbulb. In fact the process took many decades, while electrical manufacturers developed machinery and equipment, generating and distribution companies formed and went about their business, and electricians established their trade. The high cost of lightbulbs limited widespread use in households and factories for many years. This problem prompted a prolonged quest to automate bulb production. Corning was slow to join the chase, however, because Amory Houghton Jr. was reluctant to tinker with the company's success with traditional craftsmanship. It fell to his sons, Alanson B. Houghton and Arthur A. Houghton, Sr. who rose to leadership of the Glass Works between 1908 and 1910, to spur the quest.

The Houghton brothers instituted significant changes at the Glass Works. They established a corporate research and development lab (one of the first in the United States) to support existing products and processes and bridge to new ones. They even formed a separate company to manufacture glassmaking machinery. During World War I, the Glass Works developed and improved generations of semi-automatic bulb-making machines with alphabetical designations. The most successful of these models, the E Machine, cranked out three times as many bulbs as the most efficient gaffers and seldom paused for a rest.

This was a time of heady expansion for the Glass Works. It purchased a glass factory in Wellsboro, Pennsylvania, and converted it to bulb production. It also acquired the Steuben Glass Company, which the noted art glass designer Frederick Carder had helped to establish in Corning in 1903. The wartime embargo on German goods opened the way for the Glass Works to manufacture more laboratory glassware, as well as to begin making optical glass. Finally, the fledgling R&D organization produced its first big winner, a tough, low-expansion, and thermally resistant glass that went to market under the brand name Pyrex. (See next section.)

The big breakthrough in bulb making came after World War I, when the race to automate resumed. By the mid-1920s, the E and F Machines and the rival Westlake machine had become standard throughout the industry. GE had begun making its own bulbs using F and Westlake machines and posed a serious threat to Corning. In response, Arthur Houghton, head of operations, and Dr. Eugene Sullivan, head of R&D, handed the development challenge to William Woods, the plant manager at Wellsboro. Woods had noticed one day that molten glass dripping through a hole in a broken shovel had formed the approximate shape of a bulb. He reasoned that a stream or ribbon of molten glass flowing continuously over a surface with appropriately spaced holes would form a series of bulbs that could be molded and cooled. Working with MIT-educated engineer David Gray and other colleagues under conditions of extreme secrecy, Woods soon perfected a "Ribbon Machine" that far outraced other bulb-making equipment.

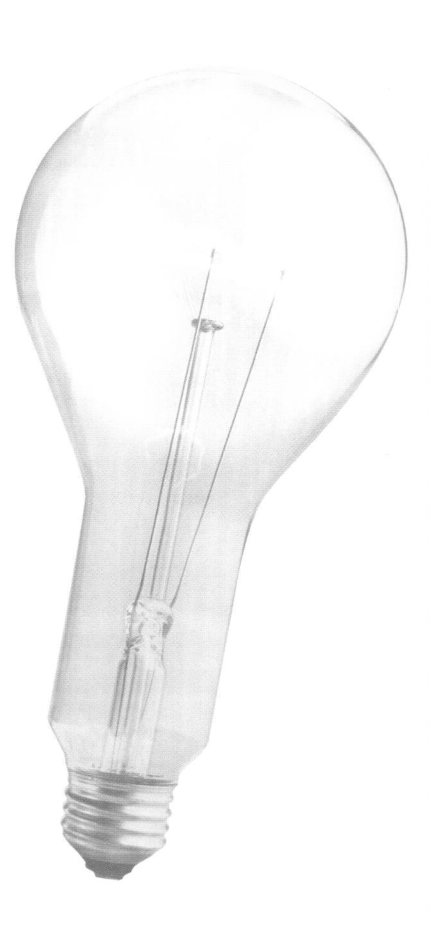

The Ribbon Machine began production in 1926 and quickly established a new standard. By the 1930s, a handful of Ribbon Machines controlled or licensed by Corning around the world produced virtually every lightbulb envelope made for decades afterward. The technology not only permitted a vast reduction in cost and brought electric light to the humblest household, but it also stimulated similar cost reductions for radio tubes and even Christmas tree ornaments.

The Ribbon Machine cemented Corning's position in the lightbulb business until the company lost proprietary control of the technology in the late 1970s. Meanwhile, Corning researchers and engineers accounted for a wide array of new glasses and shapes for specialized markets in illumination. In the 1920s, the company had become a leading producer of glass tubing for neon signs. In the next decade, Corning engineers improved the Vello process—a European method of making large-diameter glass tubes—and stimulated the spread of fluorescent lighting. In the following decade, Drs. Harrison Hood and Martin Nordberg developed a very strong, very pure glass called Vycor that proved ideal for high-intensity and high-temperature lighting systems. In the 1950s Corning expanded its small business with the automobile industry by pioneering molded glass lenses and reflectors for sealed-beam headlights. These products provided a powerful, three-fold advantage: better illumination, reduced leakage, and simpler assembly.

Although Corning sold its lightbulb envelope business to customers in the early 1980s, nearly twenty years later it remains a significant producer of glass for illumination. Today, Corning glass appears in automobiles, street lamps, light houses and airport beacons, and many specialized lighting applications.

Corning gaffers blew early lightbulbs by hand. At peak capacity, a skilled craftsman could produce several hundred bulbs per day. Pictured: In 1929—50 years after the fact—Frank Hultzman Sr. and Frederick Deuerlein reprise their roles in blowing early bulbs for Thomas Edison.

Within ten years, lightbulbs accounted for a majority of Corning's business and prompted several expansions of the Main Plant. Pictured in 1889 amid the floodwaters of the Chemung River, the plant illustrated a flourishing business, as well as a periodic reminder of its vulnerability to natural disaster.

In the aftermath of the flood, the factory was rebuilt and expanded again. The rectangular tower in the center-left of the image indicates another source of growth in the 1890s—tubular glass for thermometers and other scientific and industrial applications.

Viewed from the east, the Crystal City showed many signs of prosperity in 1900. The Glass Works, with its stacks, is visible at the far right of the image.

Masons prepare to work on the refractory brick linings of a furnace. The ceramic bricks had to withstand hellish temperatures and remain inert in the presence of molten glass. Corning later manufactured bricks for its own use and for other materials and metals companies at its subsidiary, Corhart Refractories.

The exterior shape of a pot furnace gave it a colloquial name—a beehive—and each furnace door was called a honey pot. Furnaces operated around the clock, and the beehive metaphor also captured the activity of gaffers and assistants in the shop.

In the 1880s and 1890s, making bulbs for lighting required a highly skilled team of gaffers and assistants. This scene from B Factory shows large bulbs taking shape on the gaffers' blowpipes.

The sons of Amory Houghton Jr.—Alanson B. Houghton and Arthur A. Houghton (left and center)—took charge of the Glass Works during the first decade of the 20th century. They also brought the company into a new era, establishing a permanent R&D laboratory and promoting automation.

When Alanson Houghton left for public service and Arthur Houghton fell ill, Elmira lawyer Alexander D. Falck (right) assumed the presidency of the Glass Works. He held the position between 1920 and 1928 and subsequently became chairman of the board until 1941.

During World War I, business at the Glass Works boomed, as the factories turned out bulbs, optical glass, and scientific glassware. Employees also supported the war effort by turning out in droves to purchase Liberty Bonds.

Signaling the company's burgeoning health in the 1920s were new administrative offices. Part of a sprawling complex at Main Plant, Building 21 served as the headquarters of the Glass Works for three decades.

In 1916, Alanson Houghton retained architect Howard Greenley to design a fashionable home high on the southern hills overlooking the Main Plant. Known as the Knoll, it featured a two-story library to house the family's impressive collection of books. When he left Corning two years later, the Knoll became home to his son Amory Houghton and his family. Subsequently it passed to the company, which today uses it for meetings and conferences.

By 1914, laboratory personnel included a dozen scientists, technicians, and assistants. The group included noted chemist William C. Taylor (third from left) and physicist Jesse T. Littleton (second from right).

An eminent geophysicist, Arthur L. Day consulted to Corning for many years, helping to gain a better understanding of glass chemistry and improve its manufacturing processes. Day maintained an extensive network of scientific contacts around the world that he tapped frequently to Corning's benefit.

William Churchill arrived in Corning in 1902 to work on improving colored glass for railroad signal lenses. He set up the company's first dedicated laboratory for optical glass, a building block for the corporate R&D laboratory established in 1908.

European-educated Eugene Sullivan joined Corning as director of research and development in 1908. During the next five decades—an especially fertile era of research and development—he and the scientists and engineers he supervised became the dominant technical force not only in the company but also in the glass industry.

The E Machine formed bulbs in a process similar to hand blowing and required skilled workers to complete the job.

In the first decades of the 20th century, Alanson and Arthur Houghton quietly funded development of new machinery to automate production of lightbulbs. Pictured below is Benjamin Chamberlin, a consulting engineer the brothers retained, in 1912 with the semi-automatic "E Machine" he helped pioneer.

The Ribbon Machine development team worked under conditions of extreme secrecy in Corning. Each night they smashed the cullet (scrap glass) to avoid leaving clues.

The completed Ribbon Machine was installed in the Wellsboro plant. Corning had acquired the plant from the defunct Columbia Window Glass Company during World War I.

Born in the year of the lightbulb's invention, William Woods, a former glassblower, developed the Ribbon Machine that revolutionized bulb making.

Before the Ribbon Machine came on line in 1926, the fastest equipment sped along at about 4,000 bulbs per hour. Woods's invention quadrupled the rate and gave Corning an insurmountable competitive advantage that endured for decades.

During World War I Corning took over the struggling Steuben Glass Works and converted part of its factory to industrial production.

The acquisition included the noted art glass designer, Fred Carder (standing near the center). The irascible and profane Carder maintained a love-hate relationship with Corning until his death in 1961.

(right) The proud developers of the Ribbon Machine posed with their creation. Seated at front are William Woods and chief engineer David Gray.

Wellsboro Gazette

LLSBORO. TIOGA COUNTY. THURSDAY. OCTOBER 14. 1920.

sboro's Chief Industry, the Corning Glass W and What It Means to Wellsboro

glass factory, which some twenty years or many years had ument to a past in- ciating in value and m of expense to its

where the molten glass, taken from the tank at about 2500 degrees fahrenheit is fashioned by the gatherers into the different size electric bulbs and handled and distributed by the nealers at their machines into the proper compartments of the crates, or hampers, in which they are transported to the

diameter from three to four inches, weighing about 15 pounds. Here the iron holding the glass is taken by the blower who inserts it for a brief moment in the small tank called the "glory hole," provided for the purpose, where the most intense heat obtains, after which, with a deft move-

constantly in action driving the gas to the different furnaces through a large pipe in which the fuel is turned over at intervals of twenty minutes from side to side of pipe, thus insuring a uniform degree of heat throughout its length. It takes a car load of coal every 24 hours to feed these

Alta Campbell
Margaret Sam
William Sulliv
Charles Decker
The hospital tendant, Anna

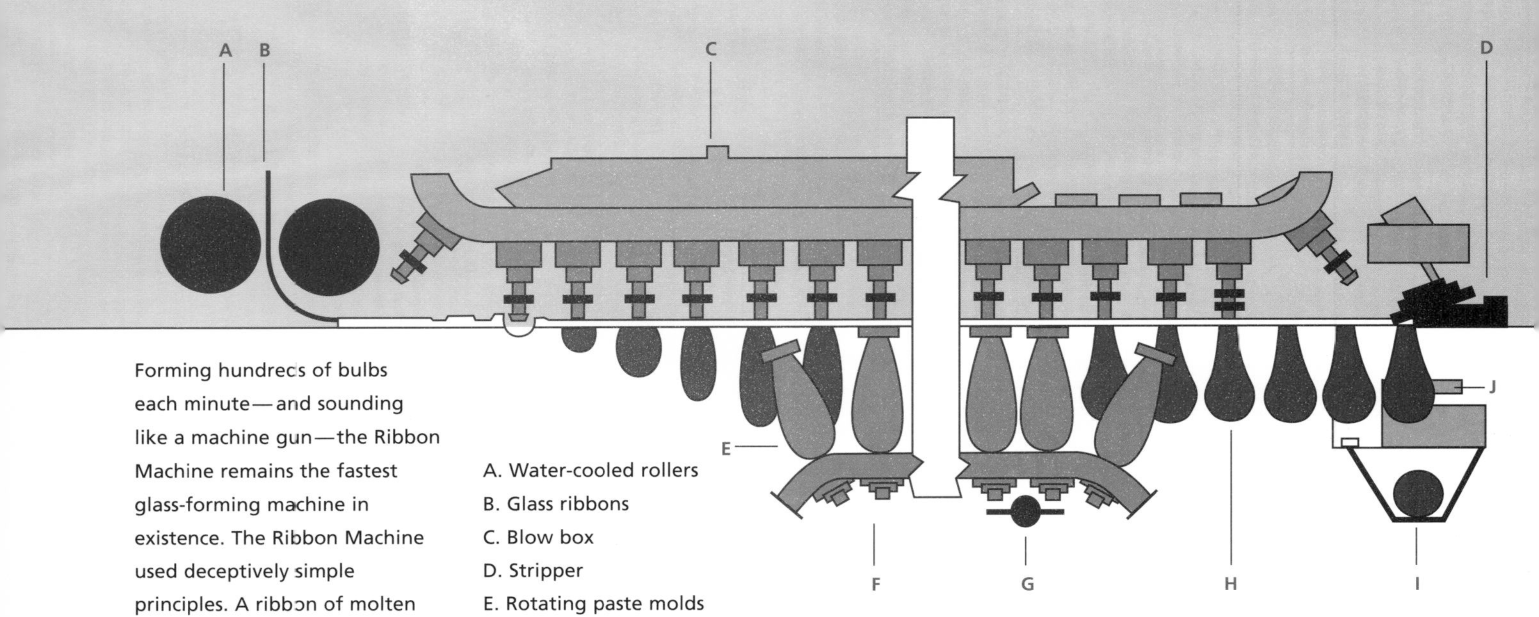

Forming hundreds of bulbs each minute—and sounding like a machine gun—the Ribbon Machine remains the fastest glass-forming machine in existence. The Ribbon Machine used deceptively simple principles. A ribbon of molten glass sagged through holes into an endless loop of molds where blasts of hot air formed perfect bulbs.

A. Water-cooled rollers
B. Glass ribbons
C. Blow box
D. Stripper
E. Rotating paste molds
F. Mold closing cam
G. Mold opening cam
H. Glass bulbs
I. Ware conveyer
J. Crack-off bar

(right) As bulbs poured off the lines, employees inspected them and aligned them for packing—a light duty job deemed suitable for female workers.

Molten glass poured into the Ribbon Machine from above, while rollers formed it into ribbons that subsequently sagged into bulb-shaped molds.

Like other glass creations, tubing was initially created by hand. In this scene from the 1870s, workers draw the tubing by stretching a gob of molten glass.

In the 1880s and 1890s, Corning gaffers drew long, thin tubing for thermometers and other delicate instruments by pulling glass horizontally over long distances. Pictured here: workers in the tube draw alley in C Factory.

Arthur Houghton Sr. took a particular interest in thermometer tubing and patented a technique for a vertical tube draw. This required a new structure, a thermometer tube tower (center, background), which Corning built in 1912. Today it remains the signature feature on the city's skyline.

In the 1920s Danner machines enabled continuous, automatic drawing of glass tubing. The resulting precise dimensions proved attractive to makers of scientific apparatus, electronic equipment, and neon signs.

The city of Corning itself proved a prominent consumer of neon signage. Here B.J. Smith, proprietor of the local cigar store, adjusts his sign as Bob Lambert, sales manager of Corning's Luminous Tube Sales Department, looks on.

Vello machines—a European technology that Corning adapted and improved upon—at Corning's Fallbrook plant proved capable of drawing large-diameter glass tubing useful in chemical plants and other process industries, as well as in fluorescent lighting.

By the 1940s, Corning glass was ubiquitous in lightbulbs, neon signs, and fluorescent lighting across the United States.

Here a technician in the company's facility near São Paulo, Brazil, prepares glass globes for street lamps.

Although Corning ceased making glass bulbs for incandescent lights in the early 1980s, it retains a vital interest in glass for illumination. Its specialty glasses are featured in many high-temperature or high-stress applications such as street lamps, while its sealed-beam head-lights remain standard items on many automobiles.

An Age of Housewares

1930-1960

In the 1930s, Amory Houghton, president of Corning Glass Works, considered renaming the company after its most famous product: Pyrex glass. Glass already had a venerable history in household products but temperature-resistant Pyrex expanded its usage from drinking vessels and dinnerware to cookware. Pyrex custard cups, pie plates, casseroles, serving bowls, measuring cups, and other pieces became staple items in American kitchens. Later Corning inventions and acquisitions —Flameware, Corning Ware, Centura, Corelle, Visions, and Revere—established the company as a force in consumer housewares. Although housewares did not become a dominant business at Corning, like glass for lighting or (later) television, it nonetheless gave the company a strong identity with the consuming public.

Pyrex originated in the search for a solution to unfulfilled needs in public services and the railroad industry. In the early 20th century, electric arc lights operated at much higher temperatures than the kerosene or gas-lit lamps they replaced. These high temperatures stressed the glass around the light source and it tended to crack or shatter in cold or rainy weather. Some types of glass—quartz glass, for example—could withstand differentials in temperature, but were expensive to produce and difficult to form. In the late 1800s, researchers in Germany developed a new "borosilicate" glass that incorporated boric oxide. The new glass was strong and featured a low coefficient of expansion, which made it unusually resistant to temperature changes, and it found growing use in streetlights. At Corning, researchers followed up on this lead. The new corporate R&D laboratory established under Eugene Sullivan in 1908 included a department devoted to hard glass. Arthur L. Day of the U.S. Geological Survey assisted Corning's studies as a consultant. The work soon yielded a lead borosilicate glass marketed under the tradenames CNX or Nonex—Corning non-expansion glass. The first applications of Nonex came in signal lanterns for the railroads.

Nonex proved so successful that it created a new problem for Corning: declining sales of lantern glass due to less breakage. The company hunted for new markets for Nonex and solicited suggestions from employees and advisers. The same properties so valuable in lanterns also seemed valuable in cookware, and some urged Corning to consider making Nonex pots and pans. The glass contained too much lead and absorbed water too readily for household cooking use, but the application was nonetheless intriguing. In 1913, Bessie Littleton, wife of newly-

Introduced as an upscale item and sold through department store channels, Corning Ware took off like a rocket. Many newlyweds began life together cooking in the Corning Ware sets they received as wedding gifts. Corning Ware also proved popular abroad, as evidenced by this display at a department store in Tokyo.

hired physics Ph.D. (and future research director) Jesse T. Littleton, suggested trying Nonex in the oven. Her husband brought home the sawed-off bottoms of two Nonex battery jars, in which Mrs. Littleton baked a sponge cake. The result was variously described as "very well cooked," "a remarkably uniform shade of brown all over," and delicious.

This success prompted serious experiments and focused development of a lead-free borosilicate glass for cookware. In 1915, Corning scientists Eugene Sullivan and William Taylor arrived at a promising new borosilicate formula. The first application was a pie plate, leading their colleague William Churchill to suggest the name "Py-right". That subsequently changed to "Pyrex" to rhyme with Nonex.

The marketing of Pyrex involved more creativity. Churchill secured the endorsements of the Good Housekeeping Institute in New York City and Sarah Tyson Rorer, the prominent editor of *Ladies' Home Journal*. The company also arranged demonstrations at (and lined up support from) leading restaurants and department stores. Corning later established its own test kitchen under Ph.D. home economist Lucy Maltby to test new products, create recipes, and collect data from consumers. During the 1920s and 1930s, the success of Pyrex cookware helped the company to weather the Great Depression.

Additional research on Pyrex yielded new uses for Pyrex in science, such as laboratory ware and telescope optics (including the 200-inch mirror blank for the Mt. Palomar observatory), and industry, such as glass blocks for construction and glass tubing in chemical plants. This work also stimulated intensified, systematic research and new advances in glass chemistry and glassmaking. Under Sullivan's direction, researchers developed a new crystal-glass formulation for Steuben and a new strong glass called Vycor; a wholly new way to make extremely pure glass by vapor deposition; and entirely new glass-based materials, such as fiberglass and silicones. J. Franklin Hyde, an organic

Physicist Jesse Littleton came to Corning in 1913, just in time to join the quest for new applications of Nonex. His wife, Bessie, conducted the first test of Nonex as ovenware in the kitchen.

chemist, proved an especially productive source of new ideas, with seminal contributions in glass chemistry and glassmaking.

Corning commercialized some innovations through joint ventures: Pittsburgh-Corning (1937, architectural glass); Owens-Corning (1938, fiberglass), and Dow-Corning (1942, silicones). These ventures launched a distinctive and enduring approach in which Corning leveraged its skills and resources and opened new areas through 50/50 partnerships with other companies.

Meanwhile, Corning itself continued to develop new glassware for consumers. In 1936, it introduced Flameware, a stovetop line of skillets, saucepans, kettles, and percolators. The new line fared moderately well. Corning had better luck when it acquired Macbeth-Evans, a glassmaker based in Charleroi, Pennsylvania. Macbeth-Evans contributed a line of attractive opal glass dinnerware, as well as know-how in automatic pressing machinery.

In the 1950s Corning at last developed a new housewares product to rival Pyrex in popularity: Corning Ware. The new product line had two parents: researcher Donald Stookey and merchandising executive Lee Waterman. After World War II, Stookey's work in photosensitive glass and Fotoform, a chemically machineable glass, had found or promised commercial applications, but an accidental discovery in 1952 proved much more valuable. While heating a piece of Fotoform, the oven in his lab malfunctioned, and temperatures soared to 900°C—about 300°C too hot. Later, as he cleaned up, Stookey found a surprise. Instead of a molten mess inside the oven, the material had retained its shape perfectly, although it had turned milky white from crystallization. When he inadvertently dropped the piece, he found a second surprise. Instead of shattering, the piece "fell on the floor like a plate of steel, and didn't break." The oven accident had produced a new glass-ceramic material with extraordinary strength and temperature resistance.

Corning dubbed the new material Pyroceram and set about to find customers. The material intrigued the U.S. military, which used it in missile nose cones because it was transparent to radiation and could withstand extreme temperatures.

A veteran in housewares merchandising at W. T. Grant and Montgomery Ward, Waterman saw another possibility: a new line of cookware suited to the changing habits of American households. In postwar America, it had become less common to bake, while families also sought convenience in cooking. In Pyroceram, Waterman believed, Corning had a material perfect for the times, capable of moving quickly and safely from the freezer to the oven or stovetop and back again. In 1958, Corning launched its new space-age cookware under its own name "Corning Ware," featuring the simple design of a small blue cornflower. During most of the ensuing decade, the product was on allocation as consumers couldn't get enough of it. A derivative line, Centura tableware, established itself as an attractive and durable product for hotels and restaurants.

Under the leadership of Amory Houghton Jr. and Waterman, Corning continued the push for new consumer products in the 1960s and early 1970s. The next breakthrough was Corelle Livingware, a laminated glass material conceptually akin to plywood. Its inventor, Jim Giffen, believed that laminated glass would make a superior building material—in roof tiles, for example. Once again, Waterman pushed applications in the housewares market, where the laminated glass was stronger and lighter than ceramic or earthenware dinner plates. Introduced in 1970, Corelle Livingware became one of Corning's strongest products during the ensuing decade.

By the mid-1980s, its housewares products constituted one of Corning's four major businesses, along with specialty glass and materials, communications products, and lab testing services. The company continued to add to its franchise through new products (Visions, a transparent pyroceram), acquisitions (Revere, a revered name in metal cookware), and innovations in distribution (the Corning-Revere factory stores).

In the 1990s, Corning's younger businesses in environmental and communications products demanded increasing management attention, and the company's interest in housewares began to wane. In 1998, Corning sold its housewares business to Borden, which operates it today under the name World Kitchen.

A great-grandson of Corning's founder, Amory Houghton became president of the Glass Works in 1930. The wall behind him represented one new line of Corning products introduced in the 1930s—glass blocks used to increase the natural light in buildings. On the desk are pieces of crystal art glass from Steuben Glass, which his cousin Arthur A. Houghton Jr. took over in 1931.

Corning's push to develop stronger glasses originated with the attempt to solve the problems of railroad lanterns, which tended to shatter when cold rain hit the hot glass surface. Corning developed a heat-resistant, low-expansion glass called Nonex that solved this problem.

Nonex also found use in battery jars. The resemblance of a battery jar when sawed off to a baking pan suggested experiments with strong glass for baking.

Technician Evelyn Roberts pours boiling water on a Pyrex casserole embedded in a block of ice. The test displayed the remarkable resistance of the glass to thermal shock—a forerunner of the "fire and ice" advertising campaign for Corning Ware in the 1950s.

At a time when most baking dishes were made of either earthenware or metal, and easily broken or hard to keep clean, or both, Pyrex had selling points that Corning promoted to the efficiency-minded housewives of the 1920s. Its transparency gave it a sanitary appearance, while the faster baking time offered savings in fuel.

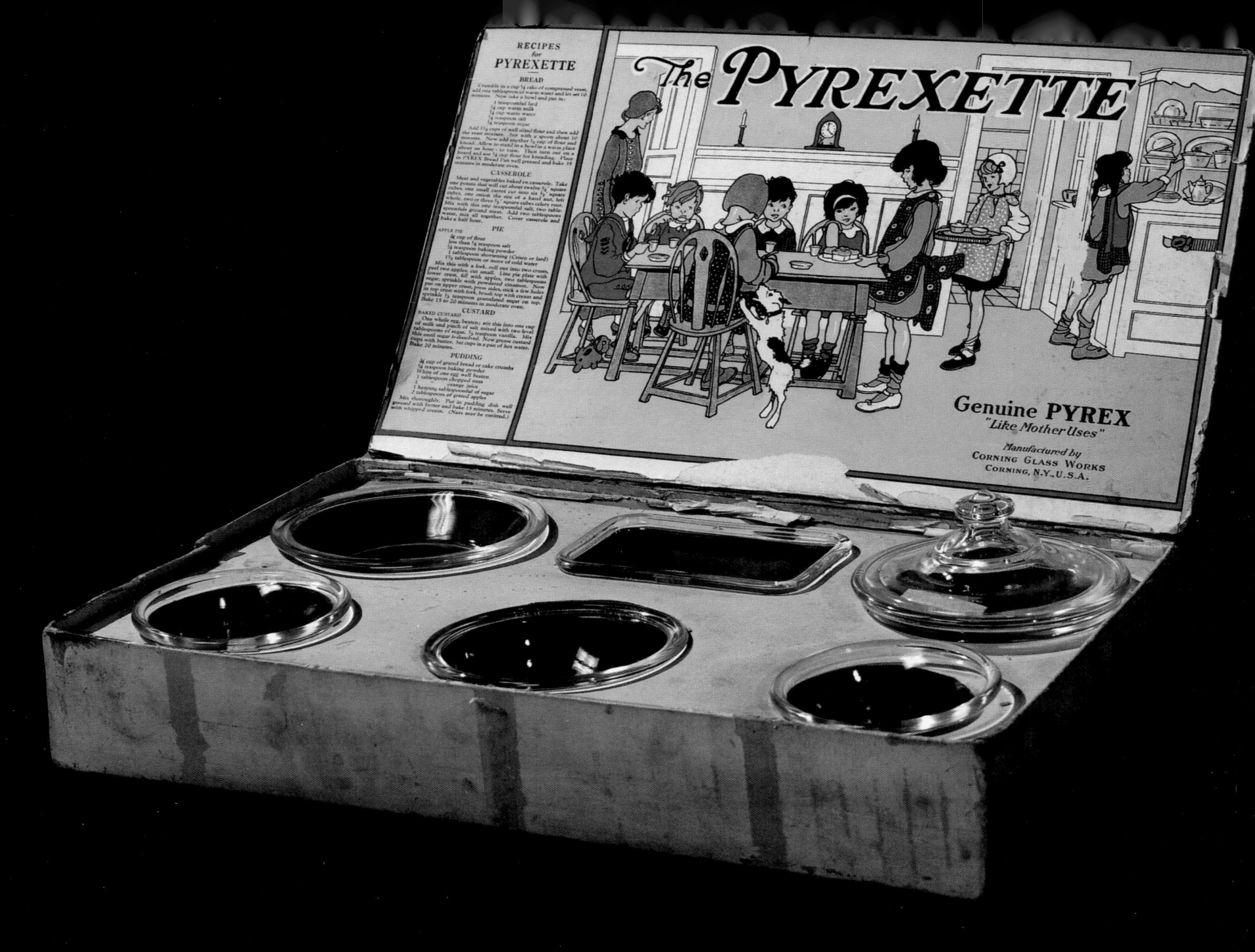

By the early 1920s, the Pyrex Ovenware line had expanded to include over sixty items, including casseroles, custard dishes, pie plates and cake pans, tea pots, bean pots, platters, and even these miniature sets made for children to use in playing house.

(right) Early Pyrex items were expensive. Promoted as gift items for upper-middle and middle-class households, they sold mainly through department stores.

With German laboratory glass-ware embargoed during World War I, Corning found a new opening for its Pyrex glass.

Pyrex glass became Corning's first significant international product, manufactured in Leaside, Ontario (above) and licensed to two companies in Europe — James A. Jobling, Ltd. in England (right) and Sovirel in France—that Corning eventually acquired.

The expiration of the Pyrex patents in the mid-1930s hastened the search for a successor. In 1936 Corning introduced Flameware, a line of products for stovetop use.

Ladies from the test kitchen observe automatic production of Pyrex custard cups at Pressware plant in 1945.

Lucy Maltby (center), a native of Corning and a Ph.D. from Syracuse University, organized Corning's test kitchen in the 1930s and directed the home economics department for three decades. Maltby's extensive correspondence with consumers and her deep understanding of how Corning's products were used in households gave her a powerful voice in designing new products.

In 1935 Corning took on a project that General Electric had tried and failed to accomplish by other, more experimental, means—to produce the largest glass disk ever cast (200-inch) as the mirror blank for the Hale Telescope on Mount Palomar.

Whereas GE had tried to produce the disk from fused quartz, Corning made its version from Pyrex, and adopted the more conventional approach of pouring the molten glass from giant ladles into a specially constructed mold.

Shipping the 200-inch disk required special precautions. Corning collaborated with the railroad to build a flatcar capable of handling the heavy load. At the same time, planners plotted a route from Corning to Pasadena, California that avoided low overpasses and antiquated bridges. The route was advertised and hundreds of thousands of people thronged to rail crossings across the country to watch the train go by.

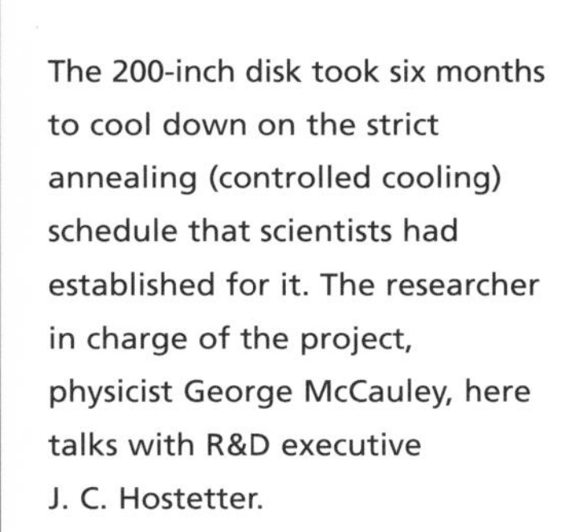

The 200-inch disk took six months to cool down on the strict annealing (controlled cooling) schedule that scientists had established for it. The researcher in charge of the project, physicist George McCauley, here talks with R&D executive J. C. Hostetter.

The disk shipped to California was the second made by Corning. The first, which had several fatal cracks, remained on display in Corning, first at an observatory built in the center of town (right; the young man walking in front is James R. Houghton, later the company's chairman and CEO), then in the Corning Museum of Glass. Today the disk is housed in the Museum's Glass Innovation Center.

In 1931, Arthur A. Houghton Jr. (left)—Amory Houghton's cousin—took over the ailing Steuben Glass Division. Together with his colleagues Jack Gates (right), an architect, and Sidney Waugh (center), a sculptor, Arthur Houghton led a turnaround based on high style and a very pure form of crystal glass.

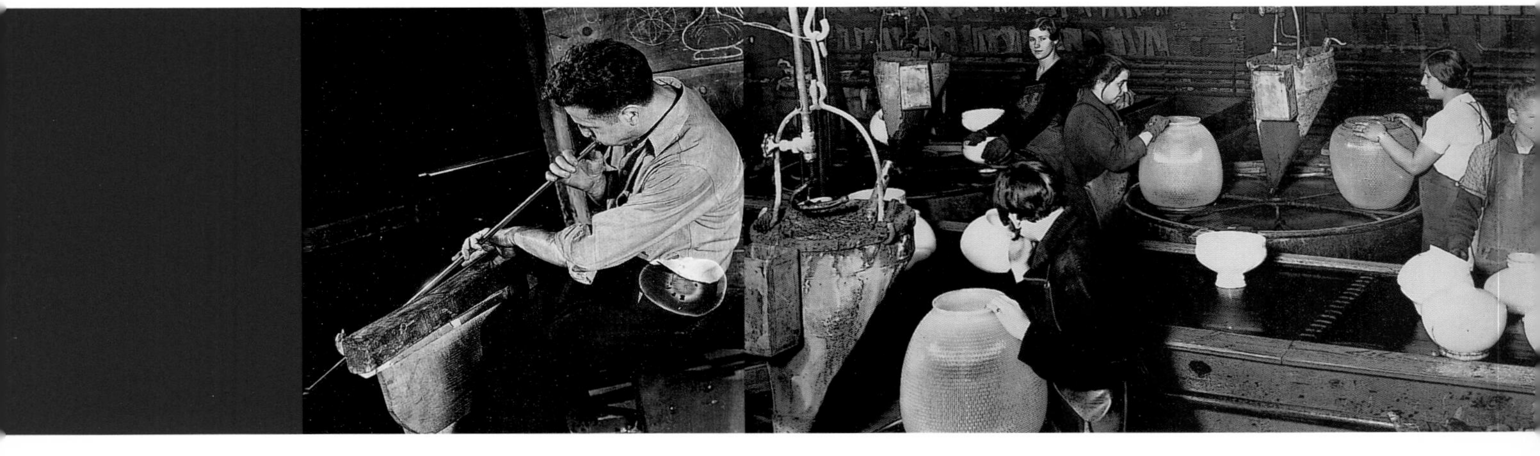

Steuben remains only a small part of Corning, but with influence disproportionate to its size. Steuben recalls the company's roots in the craft of glassmaking, as well as its commitment to products of the very highest quality.

Pictured: gaffer Charles Sullivan works on a Steuben piece in 1940.

In 1936, Corning merged with the Macbeth-Evans Company of Pittsburgh, a maker of specialty glass products with a history that paralleled Corning's. The deal included Macbeth-Evans's factory in Charleroi, Pennsylvania. This scene depicts the grinding of large lantern globes at Macbeth-Evans, c.1920.

Macbeth-Evans's product line (pictured below in the company's showroom about a decade before its acquisition by Corning) included lamp glass and opal glass dinnerware.

The company also possessed an outstanding technical reputation and maintained a strong relationship with the research center of the Mellon Institute.

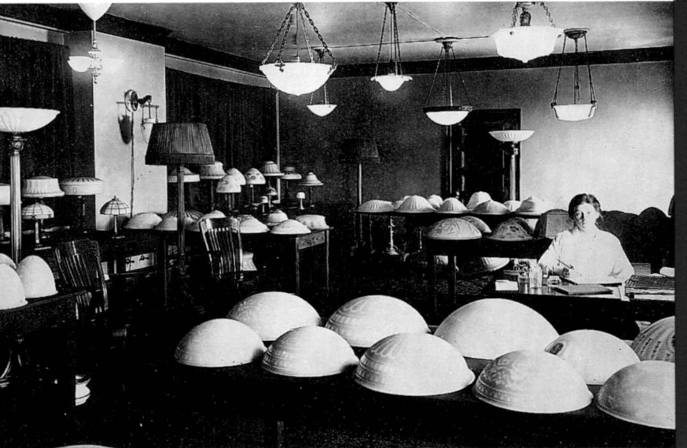

Another asset acquired in the merger was George D. Macbeth, who joined Corning's board of directors and the executive ranks as chief controller. Macbeth overhauled the company's financial reporting systems and gave Corning a much better understanding of its costs.

Corning adopted Macbeth-Evans's corporate logo—a glassblower dubbed "Little Joe"—as its own. Although Corning abandoned the logo when it changed its corporate name in 1989, Little Joe lives on as a symbol atop the thermometer tower in the company's home city.

Still another new product line—and the basis of another joint venture—was fiberglass. In 1938, Corning and Owens Illinois joined forces to create Owens-Corning Fiberglas to develop the new technology.

A promising new market for glass was architecture, especially the modernist designs sweeping in from Europe. Corning crafted these panels of Pyrex for installation at New York's Rockefeller Center. Here Fred Carder, sculptor Attilio Piccirilli, and David Gray inspect the panel for installation above the main entrance to the International Building East.

Corning also fabricated building blocks from Pyrex. In 1937, the company joined with Pittsburgh Plate Glass to form Pittsburgh Corning, a joint venture to produce glass blocks and other products for the building trades. This was the first of many long-standing joint ventures between Corning and partners with complementary skills and resources.

The 1930s proved a fertile decade for research at Corning. Among the most prolific researchers was Frank Hyde, pictured here with Mary Purcell Roche. An organic chemist, Hyde developed silicones — a new cross between glass and plastic — that became the basis of the Dow Corning Corporation, Corning's joint venture with Dow Chemical Company. Other Hyde inventions included the process for making pure glass by vapor deposition—central component of Corning's later success in optical communications.

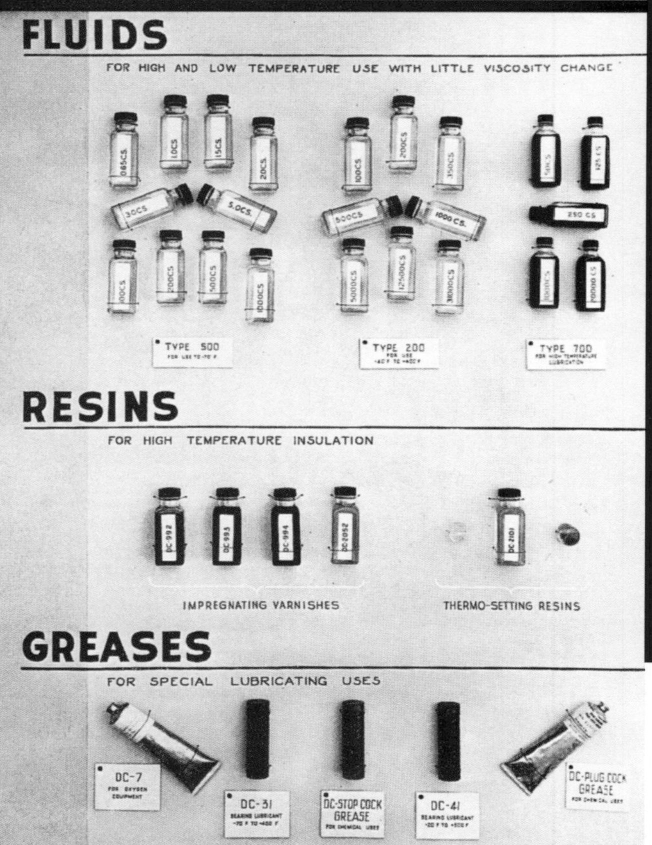

Dow Corning's silicone-based products proved important in the war effort, improving the performance of electrical motors aboard aircraft and ships.

In May 1943, Corning agreed that the American Flint Glass Workers Union—the Flints—would represent its hourly workers throughout the company. The first contract, covering the plants in the Chemung Valley, was signed in January 1944. The central figures at the signing were Harry Cook, president of the Flints (second from left), and Harry Hosier, Corning's vice president of industrial relations (second from right).

Amory Houghton took a leave of absence from the Glass Works to work as a "dollar-a-year" man as a senior executive at the War Production Board in Washington. Later he served as Deputy Chief of the U.S. Mission in London.

While he was a way, his brother-in-law, Glen Cole, served as acting president of the company. An able executive, Cole also had a common touch with employees. He was "the best personnel man I ever saw," said one admirer.

In 1951, Corning celebrated its centennial by establishing the Corning Foundation and the Corning Museum of Glass—a major tourist attraction in the Southern Tier. Arthur Houghton Jr., Amory Houghton Sr., and architect Wallace K. Harrison pose with model of the science and industry center at the museum.

Merchandising executive Lee Waterman (left, pictured with Amory Houghton Jr.) believed that Pyroceram would make a terrific material from which to make cookware. He was right, and the phenomenal success of Corning Ware helped propel Waterman to the presidency of the Glass Works.

In 1957, Corning opened a new office and laboratory complex on the north bank of the Chemung River. Amory Houghton Jr. spoke at the dedication in June. The office tower, C Building, served as the company's executive offices until 1993.

Stookey Gets Copy of Patent Issued to Him for Pyroceram

• Dr. S. Donald Stookey has been presented a copy of the first patent issued him relative to the invention of Pyroceram glass-ceramic materials.

President William C. Decker congratulated Dr. Stookey as he presented him the patent papers.

Dr. Stookey is manager of the company's Fundamental Chemical Research Dept.

Decker said that "during the 30 years of my association with the company, the invention of Pyroceram has been the single most important achievement in our research laboratories."

Discovery of the material, he said, "has given birth to an entire new industry and we have hardly begun to exploit the full potential of the new materials."

Announcement of the new family of ceramics which are made from glass was made in May, 1957.

Since that time, the company has produced radomes of the material and has introduced Corning Ware, a line of cooking-ware.

Decker pointed out that many groups within the company performed outstanding jobs in translating the material from the laboratory to full-scale production in less than 1½ years after its initial discovery.

DR. S. D. STOOKEY

issued Dr. Stookey for this first phase of Pyroceram development.

This is Stookey's 23rd patent. He has 20 in his own name, three held jointly, and eight pending.

Several other Corning men have succeeding patents on Pyroceram pending with the Patent

In the mid-1950s, Corning produced its next hit in consumer housewares: Corning Ware. The product originated in a laboratory accident. A superheated piece of photosensitive glass when cooled turned milky white and proved surprisingly durable. The serendipitous inventor, Donald Stookey, had created a new family of materials: glass ceramics.

Dubbed Pyroceram, the new glass ceramic material intrigued the U.S. military, which prized its strength and resistance to thermal shock. Jim Giffen (above) developed a process to form Pyroceram into radomes (nose cones) for rockets and missiles.

Like Pyrex before it, Corning Ware proved a product right for the times. Stronger and more durable than Pyrex, Corning Ware could move quickly between the oven and the freezer and back again—desirable properties in a new age of convenience cooking.

To keep its line of Corning Ware fresh, the company introduced new designs and products, such as coffee percolators. Despite a product recall, many satisfied customers refused to part with their pots.

(below) In 1960, Corning opened a new factory in Martinsburg, West Virginia, to make Corning Ware pieces. The factory was later expanded and modified to make Visions—a transparent glass ceramic—as well as Corning Ware.

Corning continued to develop new products from Pyrex in the 1960s and 1970s. In the 1960s, it expanded its factory in Muskogee, Oklahoma, to make Pyrex coffee pots such as those used in restaurants and cafes.

The pots were blown in high volume on the Turret-Chain Machine—another Corning invention.

Introduced in 1970, Corelle Livingware proved a sensation. The product remained on allocation throughout the decade.

The resourceful Jim Giffen made another signal contribution to Corning by developing ways to work a lightweight and strong laminated glass. Giffen first expected to use the laminated glass as a building material. Instead, thanks to his patented Hub Machine, it became a best selling source of dinnerware: Corelle Livingware.

Corning sought to augment sales of glass housewares in the late 1980s by acquiring Clinton, Illinois–based Revere Ware, Inc. By adding Revere's distinctive line of metal cookware, Corning bolstered its distribution in department stores and broadened the appeal of its own factory stores.

In the 1980s, Visions seemed a winner in housewares comparable to Corning Ware. The company couldn't make it fast enough until 1989, when the market abruptly cooled.

In the 1970s, Corning had struggled with a product introduced before its time: The Counter That Cooks, a rangetop surface made of Pyroceram.

In 1994, the company joined with St. Gobain to form a venture called EuroKera, which reintroduced the product. In the late 1990s, EuroKera became one of Corning's most promising specialty materials businesses.

An Age of Electronics

1960-1975

The transparency of glass is its most obvious feature, but it is also one that works to slight its material contributions to industrial society. Just as glass played a vital but unseen role in the development of electric lighting, so it reprised that role in the development of the electronics industry. Glass works well in electronic applications not because it is transparent, but because it is durable and an excellent insulating material. Corning proved very resourceful in developing glass compositions and forms for the electronics industry. Indeed, it's not too much to say that the electronics revolution depended as much on materials as on better understanding of electrons, and that Corning made indispensable, albeit hidden, contributions to the revolution.

Corning's involvement with electronics reaches back to the early 20th century, when it manufactured glass envelopes for vacuum tubes in primitive radio equipment. Gaffers blew the bulbs by hand and made small quantities. The advent of the Ribbon Machine (see p. 34), used primarily to make light bulb glass, proved an immense boon to the radio industry. Corning had produced 40,000 receiving tube bulbs in 1910; in 1933, when it began using the Ribbon Machines to manufacture radio bulbs, it produced 300 million. In the process, the prices of radio sets plummeted, and radios became ubiquitous in American households.

Later in the 1930s, Corning also began producing large glass bulbs for cathode ray tubes (CRTs) for new test equipment such as oscilloscopes, as well as for experimental television sets. A CRT is essentially a big vacuum tube, with a flat side or faceplate. The interior of the faceplate is coated with phosphors that glow when hit by a stream of electrons—the basic principle of television reception. Corning proved adept at making CRTs, and its 9-inch circular bulbs went on display at RCA's futuristic demonstration of television at the 1939 World's Fair in New York City. These early CRTs were hand blown in small batches, and it was a delicate operation to produce them in the right shape. The outbreak of World War II brought new urgency to the production of CRTs, which became "the glass heart" of radar sets. The government's high-volume requirements stimulated an intensive search for new ways to make CRTs. In 1943, Ed Guyer developed an electrical process to seal bulbs from two component pieces, the funnel and the faceplate. This timely innovation enabled the company to manufacture more than three million CRTs by the end of the war.

Glass bulbs for TV sets constituted Corning's major business in the 1960s and 1970s. Starting with black-and-white bulbs after World War II, the company graduated to the more demanding and popular color bulbs in the 1960s. Along with Corning Ware and some emerging electronic products, color TV bulbs reinforced Corning's image as a space-age manufacturer. The image displayed on the set here, drawn from a company advertisement, features visitors to the Corning Museum of Glass viewing the first 200-inch disk for the Mt. Palomar telescope.

In the late 1940s, Corning continued to work on mass producing large glass bulbs for the fledgling television industry, which was about to experience phenomenal growth. In 1947, approximately 200,000 Americans owned TV sets; three years later, the set makers sold 10 million units. Corning anticipated this boom and, under the leadership of President William Decker, added capacity ahead of demand. In 1948 the company converted portions of Pressware and Main Plant to make TV glass. Two years later, it built a new TV glass plant in Michigan. Meanwhile, Corning made significant advances in glass composition and bulb production. William Armistead developed a new lead-free glass formula for the faceplate and funnel that resulted in lighter bulbs with the desired electrical properties. Jim Giffen, a self-taught mechanical engineer, devised an ingenious process to make the awkward funnel shapes by spinning molten glass into a mold. Together, these innovations enabled Corning to become the biggest independent producer of TV glass in the world. During the 1950s and 1960s, Corning rode the explosive growth of the television industry, along the way learning to make larger bulbs and rectangular shapes. The company also established a lead in producing bulbs for color TV sets. TV glass for black-and-white and color sets bore obvious similarities, but also crucial differences. Color bulbs, for example, required different electrical properties, which in turn meant new compositions and manufacturing processes. The faceplates on color bulbs had to be ground with extreme precision to accommodate the layered coatings of phosphors. Finally, changes in bulb composition, design, and production made sealing the funnels and faceplates a more daunting challenge, especially since bulbs were prone to break in shipping. In 1963, Corning's Stewart Claypoole developed a new frit that enabled customers to assemble and seal bulbs in their own plants. This innovation both lowered costs and reduced breakage.

Corning poured money from its lucrative TV glass business into research and development to identify future applications of glass, glass ceramics, and ceramics. In 1962, R&D personnel moved from Houghton Park in Corning to a new complex, Sullivan Park, high on a hill in Erwin, overlooking the Chemung Valley. Envious executives still working downtown called the complex "the Ponderosa" after the prosperous Nevada ranch in the hit television series, "Bonanza."

In the 1960s, Corning produced 125 percent of its customers' needs for TV glass—all of their bulbs and then some to accommodate breakage. New plants opened in Canada, Indiana, and Pennsylvania. At the same time, the booming TV business hastened the company's growth overseas. As its customers set up facilities abroad, Corning followed to serve their needs. The company acquired its licensees in France and the United Kingdom and licensed its technology in Japan, South America, and several East Bloc countries. As Amory Houghton Jr. assumed increasing responsibilities atop Corning (president, 1961–1964; chairman and CEO 1964–1983), the company accelerated international sales in all its product lines. It formed a new International Division and between 1966 and 1975, under the successive leadership of Robert D. Murphy (a former Undersecretary of State), Forrest Behm, and James R. Houghton, the company's international sales soared tenfold to account for a third of corporate revenues.

Although TV glass accounted for most of its electronics-related growth—as well as its overall growth—Corning also manufactured electronic components for use in military and commercial applications. The company had begun making resistors and capacitors using high-purity glass during World War II, when mica from India was unavailable. After the war, the company continued to produce these components and added another: delay lines used in radar systems. In 1957, Corning formed an Electronics Division to oversee these products, and in the next decade the company built three new plants and established an R&D lab for electronics in Raleigh, North Carolina. The company attempted to move beyond components into systems and by the late 1960s was working on developing its own brand of computer terminals. Corning also acquired a majority interest in Signetics, a start-up producer of integrated circuits based in Sunnyvale, California. Drawing on Corning's investment capital, Signetics launched on its own growth spree, adding new plants in the United States, Korea, and Europe developing new products at the frantic pace customers and competitors demanded.

In the early 1970s, a series of forces checked the rapid expansion of Corning's electronics business. An industry shakeout in semiconductors prompted the sale of Signetics in 1975. Corning also discovered, painfully, that it could not afford to compete as a systems supplier in electronics. The company withdrew from attempts to make electronic equipment and focused on making components. A more serious and unsettling crisis followed, the rise of the Japanese consumer electronics industry to global dominance. As Corning's U.S.-based customers for TV glass fell by the wayside, the company's business suffered an irreversible decline. The energy shock of 1973-1974 compounded these troubles and pushed Corning into a major corporate restructuring involving the first plant closings in its history and the first large-scale layoffs since the Great Depression. Although the company joined with the American Flint Glass Workers and other U.S. business and labor groups to achieve temporary import quotas on Japanese TV sets, the reprieve did not address underlying problems in the American industry. By the early 1980s, the company had closed all of its black-and-white TV facilities and produced all of its color TV glass in a single plant in State College, Pennsylvania.

The setbacks of the mid 1970s forced a fundamental reassessment of Corning's strategy and led to a focus on newer industries such as medical equipment and services, environmental products, and communications products. At the same time, Corning revamped its strategy in electronics products, exiting the components business in 1987 and redefining the TV glass business as part of a new thrust in information displays. In 1988, the company formed a joint venture with Asahi Glass to produce TV glass in State College, Pennsylvania for Japanese set manufacturers. In 1994, Corning and Asahi joined with Sony to establish another TV-glass joint venture, American Video Display. Samsung Corning, a joint venture with Korea's Samsung established in 1973, became a major global producer of TV glass as the Korean consumer electronics industry challenged the Japanese for world leadership.

Corning also focused on promising new areas of growth in information displays. In 1986, the company acquired U.S. Precision Lens, the leading producer of lens systems for projection TVs. Still more opportunities followed the rise of personal computers. Corning's Fusion Process for making flat glass did not prove economical for windows but it was ideally suited for the liquid crystal displays on notebook computers and other electronic equipment and devices. By the early 1990s, Corning was the leading producer of LCD glass in the world, with operations in Harrodsburg, Kentucky, and Shizuoka, Japan.

Bill Armistead guided research and development at Corning between the mid-1950s and the mid-1980s as director of research and vice chairman with responsibility for technology. A distinguished glass chemist, he held important patents on TV and optical glass. Here he holds a piece of massive glass, a product engineered for the U.S. Navy for use in experimental underwater vehicles.

Five presidents of the Glass Works gathered for the 95th anniversary of the Wellsboro plant in 1946. The group included (left to right) Alexander Falck, Amory Houghton Sr., Bill Decker, Glen Cole, and Eugene Sullivan. Pictured at the far right is George Macbeth.

The flag behind the officers at left is made of Christmas ornaments produced on the Ribbon Machine.

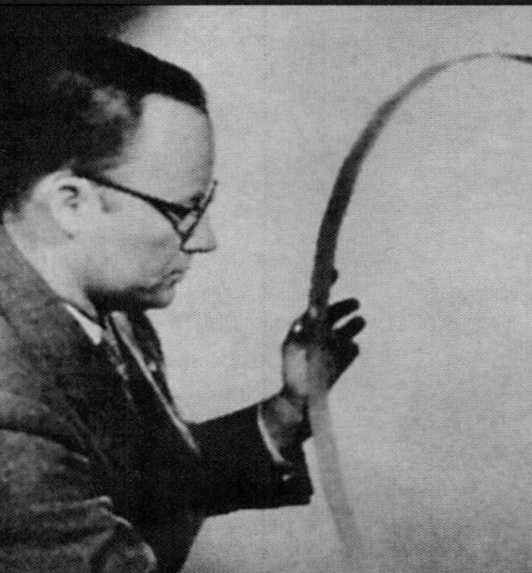

Bill Decker served as president of the Glass Works from 1946 to 1961 and as chairman of the board from 1961 to 1964. During his tenure, Corning committed wholeheartedly to new businesses in electronics and TV glass.

Corning's first products for the electronics industry—radio tubes and radar bulbs—represented a natural extension of its longstanding expertise in making bulbs for lighting.

The management team that presided over Corning's booming growth in TV glass and electronics included (left to right) Forrest Behm, Al Dawson, Amory Houghton Jr., and Malcolm Hunt.

Shapes of things to come: The first TV bulbs were small and round. Gradually, they grew in size and shifted into familiar rectangular shapes.

Fabricating the faceplate involved pressing a molten gob of glass into a mold.

Making the funnel posed more difficulties. These pieces were awkward to press, so self-taught mechanical engineer Jim Giffen devised an ingenious way to spin molten glass into the proper shape. A researcher claimed the process would never work. "I've already made it work," Giffen retorted.

The innovation enabled Corning to make glass funnels competitive in price with metal funnels used by some set manufacturers. Eventually, as TV sets grew larger, glassmakers learned to press funnels, the standard practice today.

By the late 1960s, TV glass had become Corning's biggest and most profitable business. The company operated four factories in North America, including color TV glass plants in Bluffton, Indiana (left), and State College, Pennsylvania, and black-and-white TV glass plants in Albion, Michigan, and Muskoka, Canada (below).

Samsung Corning's H.C. Shin believed that one day Korean manufacturers would rival the Japanese in consumer electronics. Like Bill Decker in the 1940s, he built production capacity ahead of demand and reaped the benefits as the business materialized.

Most of Corning's involvement in electronics reflected its expertise in making glass bulbs. In the 1950s and 1960s, however, the company used glass materials in a variety of electronic components.

Delay lines, for example, were used in radar systems. Corning formed these products from fused silica, the production process that would become the basis of optical fibers.

Chemist Tom MacAvoy joined Corning's R&D organization in 1956. His versatility and quick study command of new subjects, including electronics, opened the pathway to the top. He moved rapidly through the ranks, serving as general manager of the Electronic Products and Technical Products Divisions before being named president and chief operating officer of the Glass Works in 1971.

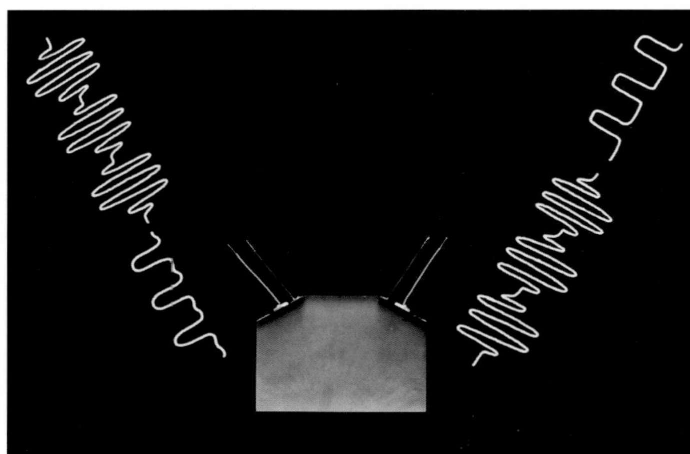

Corning's farthest reach into electronic products involved the Corning Model 904 computer terminal. The company manufactured a handful of units in 1970 but its reach exceeded its grasp.

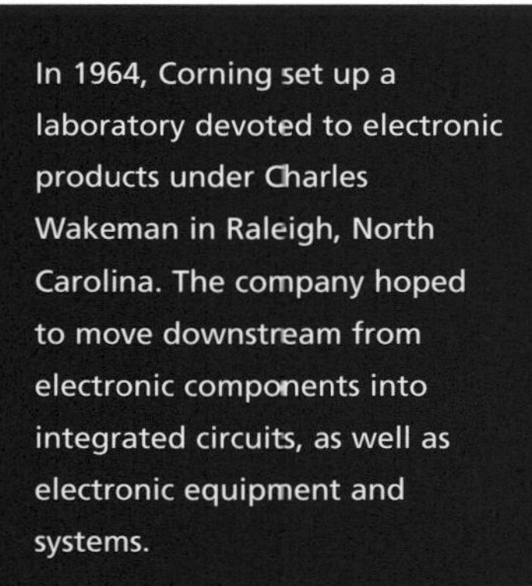

In 1964, Corning set up a laboratory devoted to electronic products under Charles Wakeman in Raleigh, North Carolina. The company hoped to move downstream from electronic components into integrated circuits, as well as electronic equipment and systems.

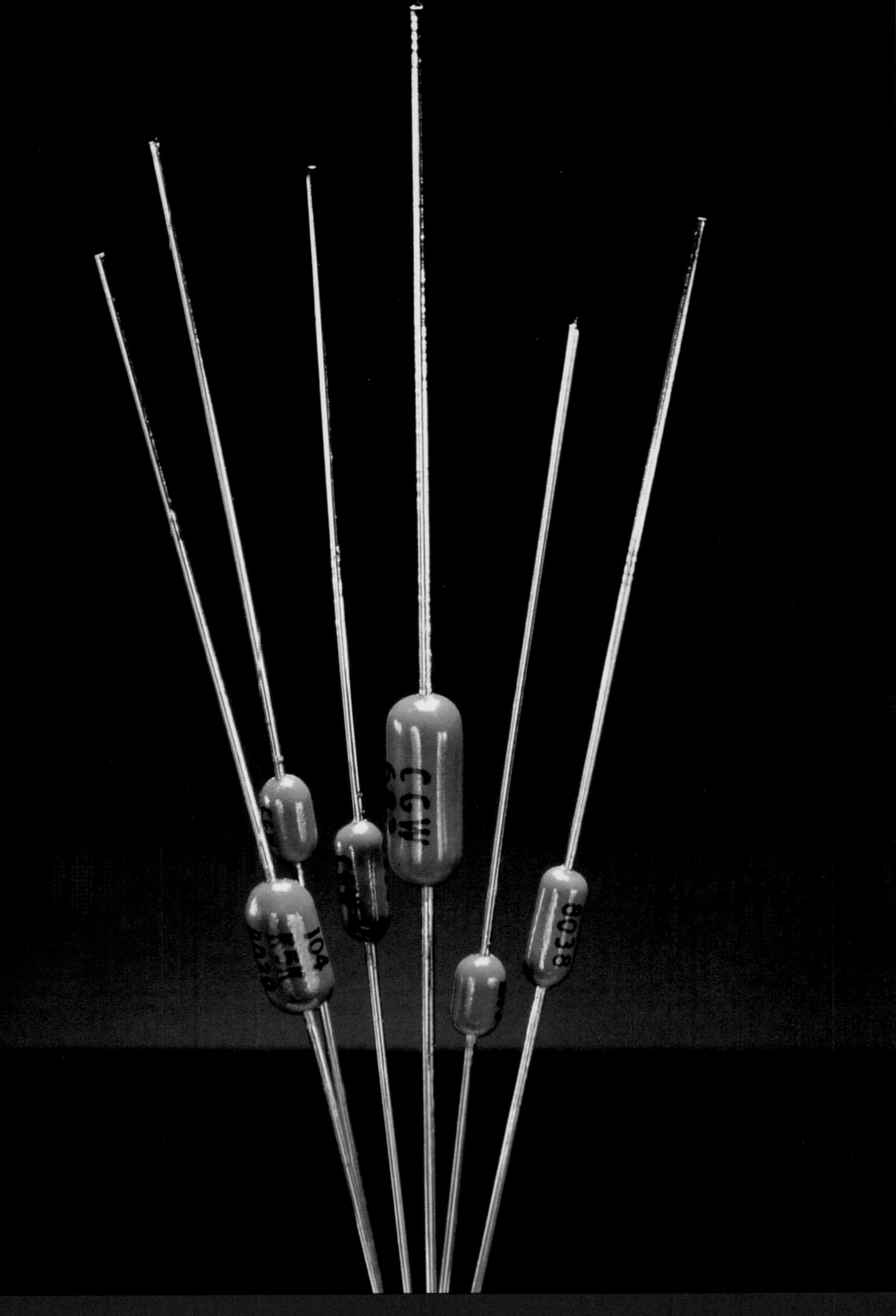

Corning manufactured resistors and capacitors at facilities in Bradford, Pennsylvania, and Wilmington, North Carolina. After a promising start, the business began to fade with the introduction of integrated circuits.

Corning acquired Signetics, a maker of integrated circuits, in 1962. The unit had a voracious appetite for investment and repeatedly taxed Corning's resources and patience. By 1975, Corning had had enough and sold Signetics to Philips.

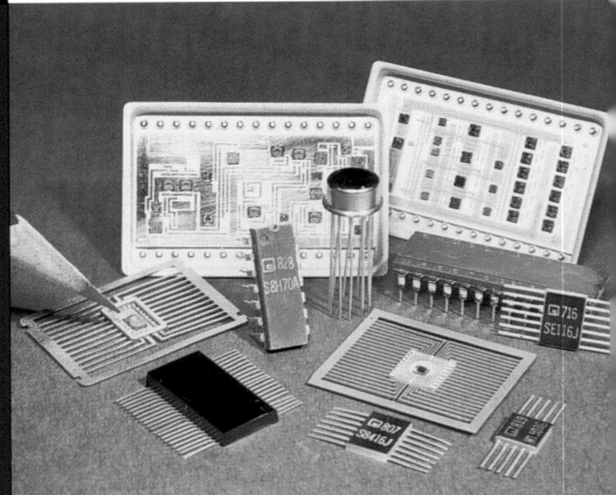

Corning acquired U.S. Precision Lens in 1986. The 36-year-old company had become the world's leading producer of plastic lens systems for projection TVs—a nice addition and complement to Corning's TV glass and LCD glass businesses.

(below) In the 1960s Corning developed a new way to make flat glass: the Fusion Process. As molten glass overflowed from a pipe, it formed perfectly smooth sheets as it cooled. Stuart Dockerty and Clint Shay (front row, fourth and fifth from left, respectively) led the team that pioneered the process.

(right) Corning hoped that the Fusion Process would enable the company to break into markets for flat glass, and targeted automotive windshields as the most promising opportunity. Just as Corning readied its first products, however, Pilkington perfected the more economical float-glass process and the opportunity vanished. The big automotive windshield opportunity was lost, but Corning used the Fusion Process to make eyeglass blanks and flat screens for liquid crystal displays at its facility in Harrodsburg, Kentucky.

The vaunted Japanese consumer electronics companies admired USPL's top quality lens systems, and the unit became one of a handful of American companies in the 1980s to gain market share in Japan.

(left) Although Corning failed to gain acceptance for its fusion-glass safety windows, the company sold a handful of units to Airstream, the producer of distinctive, upscale trailers.

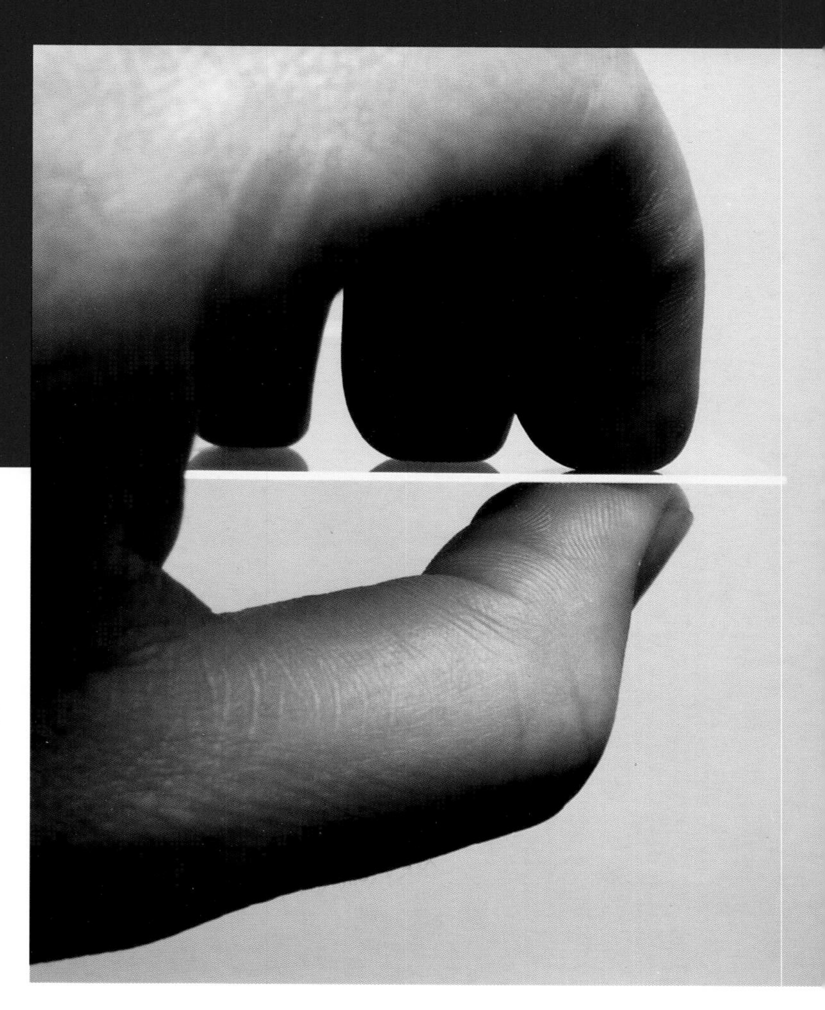

The thin and perfectly smooth glass sheets produced by the Fusion Process proved ideal for a fast-growing application in flat panel displays and LCD glass. Corning projects that LCD glass will remain a major business well into the 21st century.

(above) Moving west across the Southern Tier, Hurricane Agnes merged with a front moving east from the Great Lakes. On June 23, 1972, following days of torrential rains, the Chemung River overflowed its banks, devastating Corning and surrounding towns.

The flood knocked Main Plant and Pressware plant out of commission and nearly destroyed the company's headquarters and the Corning Museum of Glass. On Market Street, the floodwaters reached four feet.

(left) The city lost power for days and some essential services for weeks. Amory Houghton Jr. went on the radio to squelch rumors that the company would leave the valley and offered the resources of the Glass Works to assist with the cleanup.

The high-water mark at the Corning Museum of Glass was sixteen feet—enough to force employees to abandon the building through the roof.

(left) In the aftermath of the flood, the company and city officials collaborated on an ambitious plan to renovate Market Street. By the mid-1970s, the street had taken on new and welcoming character as new shops and restaurants moved in.

In the aftermath of the flood, the city of Corning was reborn with major renovations to Market Street. Downtown Corning today is a noted tourist attraction that offers an inviting glimpse into small town America.

The British subsidiary, James A. Jobling, Ltd., became Corning Ltd., adding production capacity in Sunderland, England, and several promising electronics businesses.

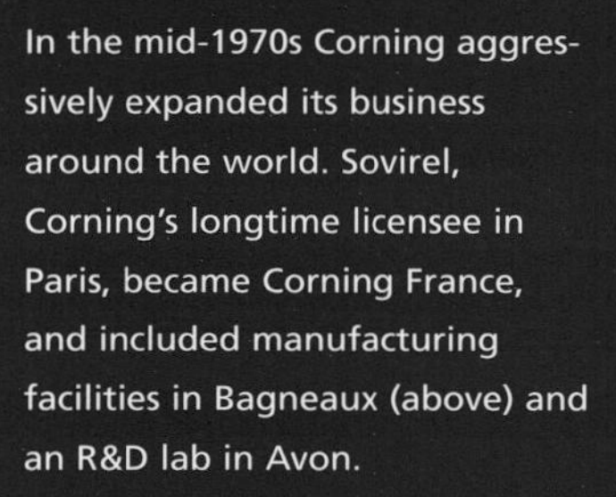

In the mid-1970s Corning aggressively expanded its business around the world. Sovirel, Corning's longtime licensee in Paris, became Corning France, and included manufacturing facilities in Bagneaux (above) and an R&D lab in Avon.

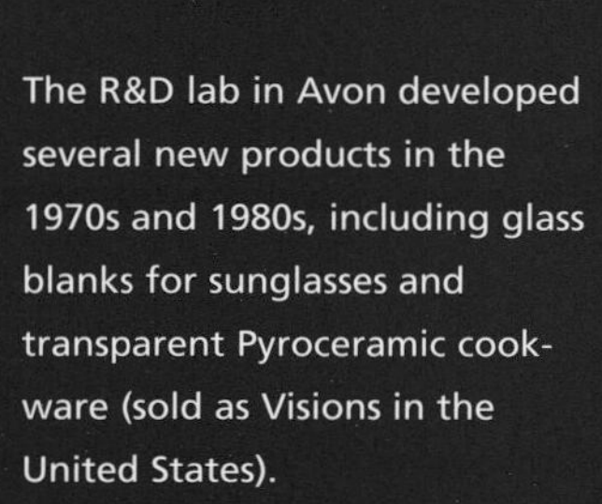

The R&D lab in Avon developed several new products in the 1970s and 1980s, including glass blanks for sunglasses and transparent Pyroceramic cookware (sold as Visions in the United States).

In 1985, Corning became one of the first American companies to open manufacturing facilities in China. This plant in Schenzhen produces glass bulbs for color TV.

Soaring demand for Corning's LCD glass among the Japanese consumer electronics companies prompted the company to build a second fusion glass facility, this time in Shizuoka, Japan. The combined output of the Harrodsburg and Shizuoka plants made Corning the worldwide leader in LCD glass.

In 1988, with Japanese TV set manufacturers building production facilities in the United States, Corning formed a joint venture with Asahi Glass to supply TV glass to the new arrivals. Corning Asahi Video specializes in making large-size color TV bulbs in State College, Pennsylvania.

When Sony set up production in the United States, it formed a new joint venture with Corning and Asahi Glass to manufacture its bulbs. Based near Pittsburgh, American Video Display supplies most of Sony's needs in North America.

One of Corning's hottest businesses, LCD glass finds its way into a dazzling variety of electronic devices, ranging from camcorders to laptop computers to portable VCRs to monitors for desktop computers.

An Age of Diversification

1975–1990

To many top executives of Corning, the collapse of the TV glass business in the mid-1970s seemed emblematic of a bigger problem: the limits of glass as the basis of continuing growth. Corning was hardly alone among U.S. manufacturers who, at the time, came to believe that their core products and technologies had reached a state of maturity and that future growth would necessarily come from new sources.

Corning did not have to look far for opportunities, and under the leadership team of Amo Houghton, Tom MacAvoy, and Jamie Houghton, it pursued them vigorously. The company's Science Products Division had already expanded from manufacturing beakers and flasks into producing simple diagnostic equipment such as pH meters. This served as a foundation for a rapid push into more sophisticated equipment for the rapidly growing health care industry. In 1973, personnel from Science Products and the Electronics Division merged into a new Medical Products Division under Marty Gibson. The new unit turned out a stream of exotic new products, including blood-gas analyzers and the overly ambitious Leukocyte Automatic Recognition Computer (LARC), a computer-based system for counting white blood cells that became one of a small number of large-scale product failures in Corning's history. Gibson and Corning achieved better results in another area related to health care: blood testing. In 1973, the company acquired a minority stake in MetPath, the biggest blood-testing laboratory in the New York City metropolitan area. The initial investment was to learn the business, which drew on Corning's lab equipment products. But lab testing had attractive structural characteristics: it served a fast-growing market; it did not consume energy; it provided services and appeared to balance Corning's traditional manufacturing operations; and it was impervious to global competition. In 1982, Corning acquired MetPath outright and used it as a platform from which to consolidate the blood-testing business nationwide. Through acquisitions, Corning Laboratory Services Inc.—the unit that comprised MetPath—became one of the biggest blood-testing units in the United States. At the same time, Corning acquired other lab testing companies—Hazleton Laboratories, G. H. Besselaar & Associates, and Enseco —to establish a growing presence in laboratory services generally. The robust health of these diverse businesses in 1989 prompted a change in the corporate name, from Corning Glass Works to Corning Incorporated.

Corning also sought to fill a niche in the burgeoning biotechnology business. In the 1970s, researchers at Sullivan Park had developed techniques to immobilize enzymes using glass membranes. The work and related research on the bonding of enzymes to glass opened new applications in health care, especially in diagnostic procedures, and in the food and beverage industries, where Corning technology could be used in processes as diverse as converting dairy by-products to sweeteners and converting red wine to white. In the late 1970s and early 1980s, Corning formed joint ventures with Genentech and Kroger Foods to develop commercial processes using immobilized enzyme technology.

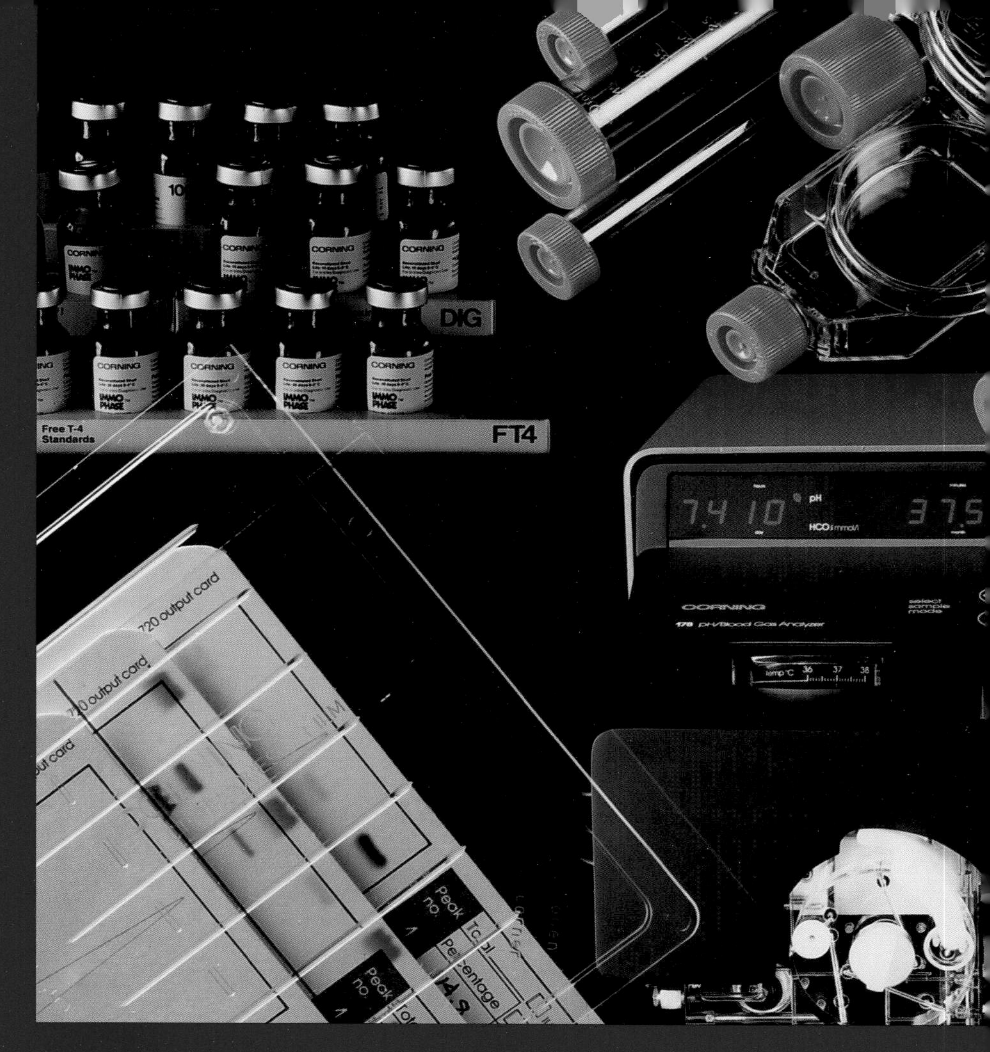

Corning's diverse ventures in medical equipment, lab testing, and biotechnology met with mixed results. By the mid-1980s it was clear that Corning lacked the resources to achieve or sustain leadership in medical equipment and biotechnology — even through joint ventures — and it sold its positions. The lab testing businesses, on the other hand, provided ample growth in revenues and cash flow during a period in which Corning was pouring investments into other new businesses, especially communications products. In the mid-1990s, however, the advent of managed health care and tighter government regulation of the lab-testing industry made long-term prospects less attractive to Corning, and it began looking for a way out. In 1996, the company arranged to spin off its lab testing properties into two separate companies, Quest Diagnostics and Covance, Inc.

The spin offs of Quest Diagnostics and Covance brought an end to Corning's age of diversification. In the meantime, several exciting new glass-based products, including optical waveguides (see next chapter), photochromic ophthalmic glass, and ceramic substrates, restored the company's faith in its core businesses. The new ophthalmic glass originated in work by Bill Armistead and Don Stookey and found application in eyeglass lenses that would darken in bright light and become clear again in normal lighting conditions. Corning promoted "Photo-Gray" and "Photo-Brown" lenses heavily and their ensuing phenomenal popularity launched the company into making sunglasses, including the upscale Serengeti brand that sizzled in the late 1980s.

During the 1970s and 1980s Corning diversified into an assortment of businesses, ranging from medical diagnostic equipment, to plastic labware, to new laboratory testing procedures, to clinical testing services. Most of these businesses were divested in the 1990s, although plastic labware anchors the company's growing presence in Advanced Life Sciences Products.

The new ceramic substrates became a much bigger hit as part of a new line of environmental products. Ironically, this healthy business had its roots in failure. During the 1960s, Corning had poured millions into the development of a new automotive windshield. Along the way, it pioneered a new process for forming perfectly smooth sheets of glass that later proved critical to making liquid crystal display glass for computers and flat-screen TV displays. But the automotive windshield was not to be, as Pilkington's float-glass process proved more economical. But the experience was hardly a bust. Intrigued by Corning's capabilities in ceramics, General Motors asked whether the company could make substrates for catalytic converters to be required on all automobiles by the 1975 model year to limit air pollution. Corning's answer was an unhesitating "yes"—although it had no time to take account of many formidable technical and managerial challenges. The company did not know how to make the substrate, much less how to produce it reliably in high volume for the automakers within four years. In the meantime, GM and other automakers were pushing alternative emissions control technologies that could well outperform catalytic converters under design.

Amid great uncertainties, Corning launched a crash program to develop a ceramic substrate. It brought deep understanding of materials and some familiarity with automotive applications from a product called Cercor that was used in experimental turbine engines. In 1971, Irving Lachman led a team of chemists that produced a workable formulation of cordierite, a ceramic made out of magnesia, alumina, and silica. Not long afterward, engineer Rod Bagley developed an extrusion process to form the ceramic into the thin-walled honeycomb structures that would form the substrates. Dave Duke, a Ph.D. in ceramics engineering, took charge of testing and manufacturing the product in volume. Duke formed cross-functional teams of personnel from research, engineering, manufacturing, and marketing and set ambitious targets for development. In January 1973, with still no confirmed orders, Corning broke ground on a new production facility in Erwin, New York. The gamble soon paid off, and Corning took orders from Chrysler, Ford, and Volkswagen. The Erwin plant began shipping the product, called Celcor, in the summer of 1974—on time for volume production of 1975 automobiles.

Celcor achieved more than $100 million in profitable sales in its first year and the foundation of a major new line of business in environmental products. At the same time, the management techniques used in developing Celcor became the model for other new product development initiatives, including optical waveguides.

After the mid-1970s, the environmental products business expanded both geographically and in range of products and services. The company added new customers for Celcor and built a second U.S. plant in Blacksburg, Virginia, noted for its high performance work systems and extraordinarily high productivity. In 1987, in anticipation of air quality standards in Europe comparable to those in the United States, Corning opened a Celcor factory in Kaiserslautern, Germany. A dozen years later, as similar standards were adopted in China, Corning built a facility in Shanghai to make Celcor for trucks.

Corning also manufactured ceramic structures as filters and substrates for a diverse array of applications, ranging from wood stoves to factories. The metals industries, for example, used ceramic filters to help purify batches of molten metal. In 1989, Corning formed a new joint venture, Cormetech, with Mitsubishi Heavy Industries Ltd. and Mitsubishi Heavy Petrochemical Company Ltd. Cormetech sold ceramic devices to electric utilities and factories to control emissions from stationary power-generating systems. In the same year, Corning acquired Enseco, an environmental testing services company that later joined with International Technology Corp. to form a joint venture called Quanterra. As Corning celebrated its 150th anniversary, environmental products represented one of the company's strongest core businesses.

In 1989, Jamie Houghton (center, wearing red suspenders) posed with a coalition of employees for the cover of Corning World, accenting the company's progress toward accommodating an increasingly diverse workforce—one of Houghton's major priorities as chairman and CEO between 1983 and 1996.

A marketing major in business school, Marty Gibson arrived in Corning with an unconventional background. His ideas were unconventional, too, but he led Corning into fast-growing new areas such as medical diagnostic equipment and laboratory services at a time when the traditional glass and materials businesses were slowing down.

Biochemist Ralph Messing discovered that proteins bond to glass surfaces, a finding with significant implications for a host of industries that rely on the action of enzymes in manufacturing processes. In the 1970s, Messing's work prepared the way for Corning to enter the industrial biotechnology business.

John Lanning (left), sales manager, and David Wardale, senior project engineer, pose with the ceramic structure they helped develop. In the 1960s, Corning fashioned ceramic structures as moving parts in gas turbine engines. Although the technology never took off, Corning's experience with the material proved invaluable when the opportunity came to make ceramic substrates.

In 1971 Jack Hutchins succeeded Bill Armistead as director of R&D. He promoted pioneering work on glass-ceramic substrates and optical waveguides and also sponsored research in new areas such as electronics and industrial biotechnology.

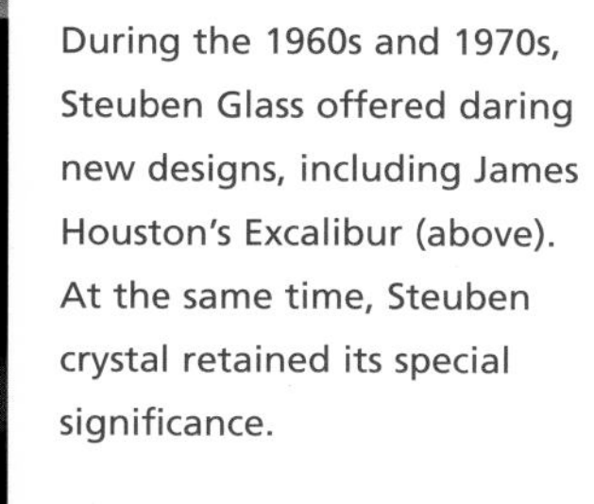

During the 1960s and 1970s, Steuben Glass offered daring new designs, including James Houston's Excalibur (above). At the same time, Steuben crystal retained its special significance.

President Jimmy Carter presented the Arcus, peace crystal, designed by Peter Aldridge, to Menachem Begin and Anwar Sadat after Israel and Egypt signed the Camp David peace accord.

Successful development of Celcor required two key technological breakthroughs. Irv Lachman (above right) found the right formula for the glass-ceramic material, while Rod Bagley engineered a new process to extrude honeycomb structures.

The Celcor substrate combined enormous surface area in a small structure — the surface area of a football field in the size of a coffee can. Coated with an extremely thin layer of platinum, the substrate fit inside a metal can. As noxious exhaust gases stream through the honeycomb structure, the catalyst triggers reactions that render the emissions harmless.

As governments around the world adopted standards for emissions control similar to those in the United States, Corning moved Celcor production abroad. In 1987, it opened a facility in Kaiserslautern, Germany, to serve the European automobile industry.

Researchers and engineers at Corning France developed a new process for forming eyeglass blanks that was adapted to making sunglasses.

Corning's ability to form ceramics into complex structures proved valuable not only for Celcor but also for a host of environmental and industrial products. Filters and substrates built by Corning and Cormetech, its joint venture with Mitsubishi Heavy Industries Ltd. and Mitsubishi Heavy Petrochemical Company Ltd., are used in heavy industry and electrical power generation.

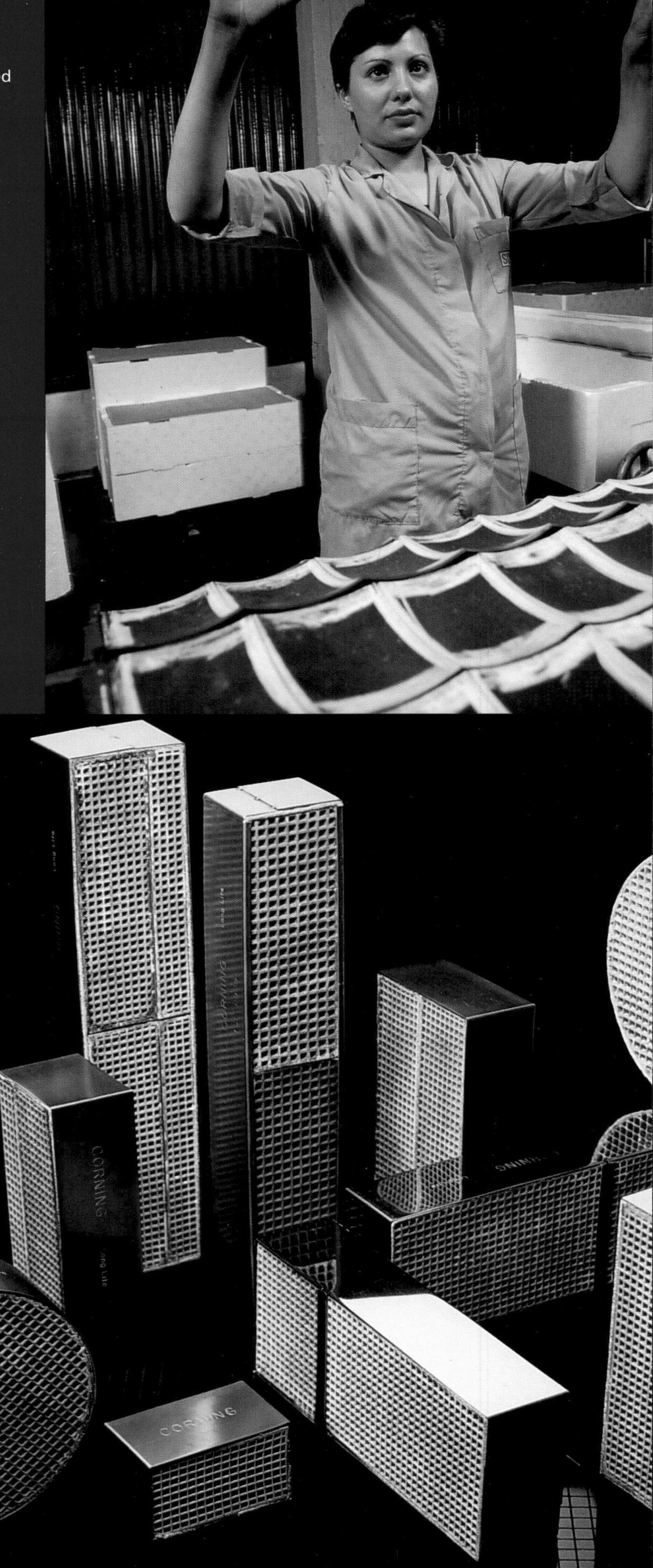

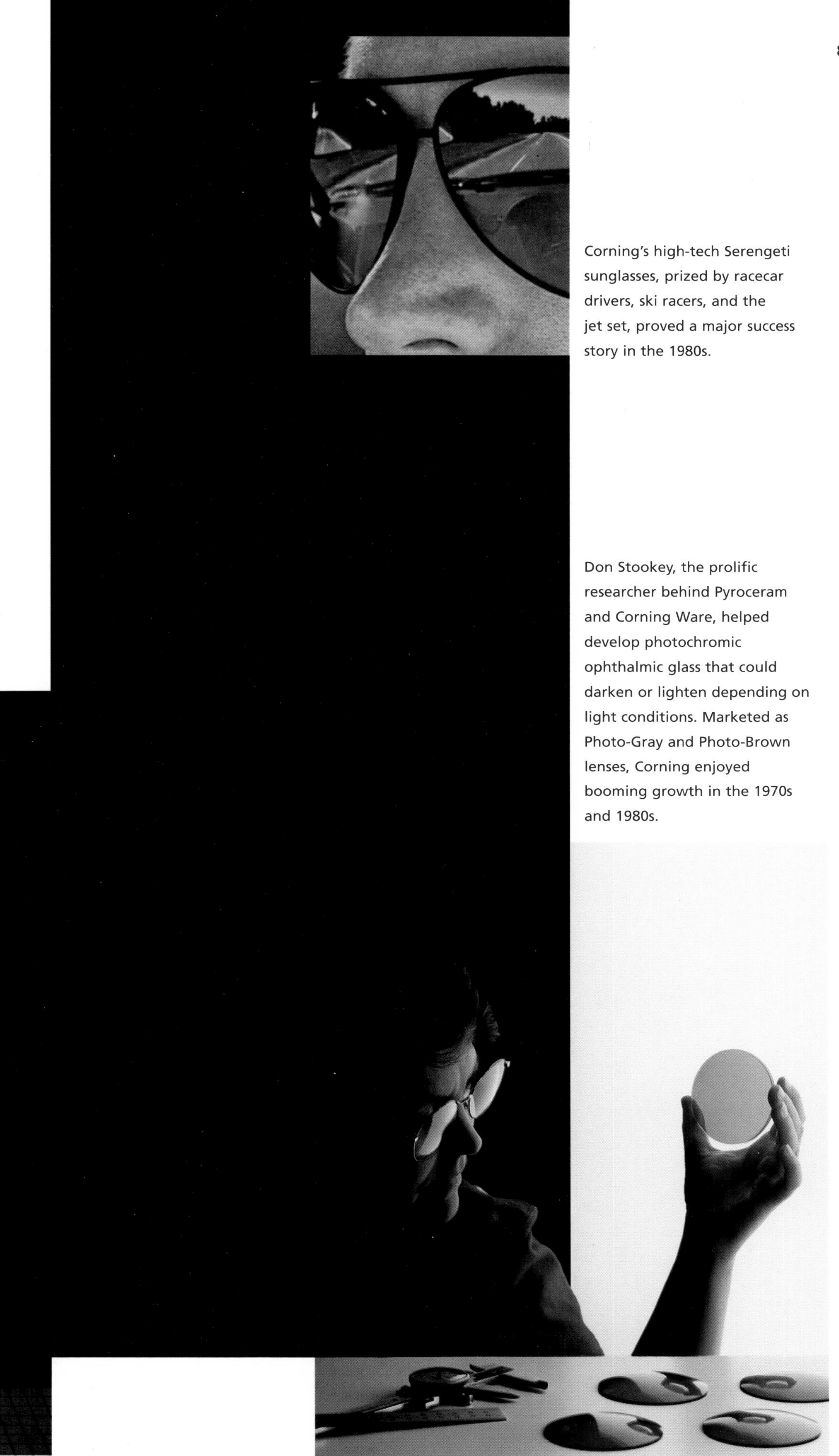

Corning's high-tech Serengeti sunglasses, prized by racecar drivers, ski racers, and the jet set, proved a major success story in the 1980s.

Don Stookey, the prolific researcher behind Pyroceram and Corning Ware, helped develop photochromic ophthalmic glass that could darken or lighten depending on light conditions. Marketed as Photo-Gray and Photo-Brown lenses, Corning enjoyed booming growth in the 1970s and 1980s.

(below) Corning's newest businesses garnered the lion's share of press and management attention in the 1960s and 1970s, but its oldest business in specialty glass remained vital.

The company supplied the glass windows for every manned U.S. spacecraft, starting with the Mercury capsules of the 1960s. Pictured below: John Glenn, President John F. Kennedy, and Vice President Lyndon Johnson inspect Glenn's Friendship 7 capsule, which orbited the earth in 1962.

As spacecraft grew through the Mercury program to the Gemini program to the Apollo and Skylab programs, astronauts continued to view the planet through Corning glass.

The mirror blank for the Hubble space telescope was manufactured in Corning's Canton, New York, facility.

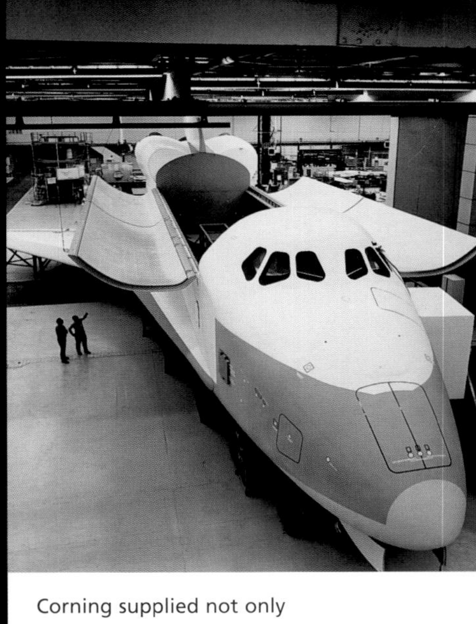

Corning supplied not only windows for the Space Shuttle (left) but also ceramic binding agents for the vehicle's skin (above).

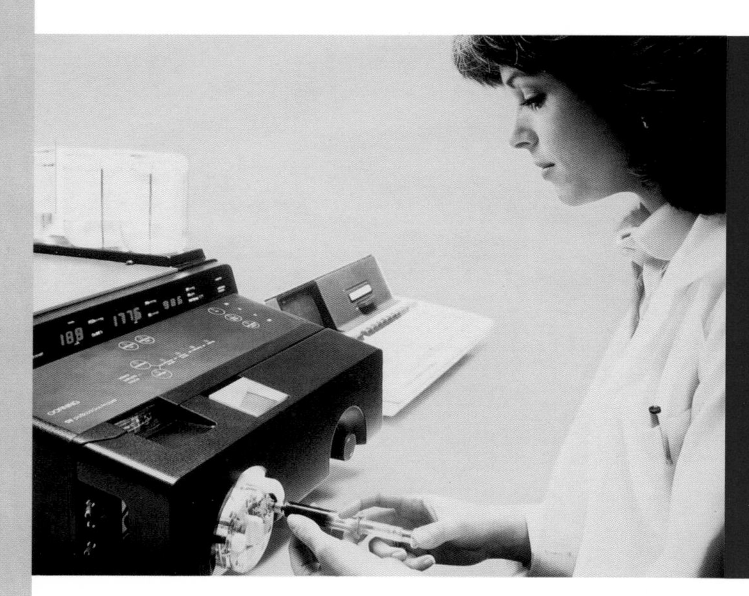

Prodded by Marty Gibson, Corning expanded its growing base in laboratory equipment, manufacturing blood-gas analyzers and other medical diagnostic machines.

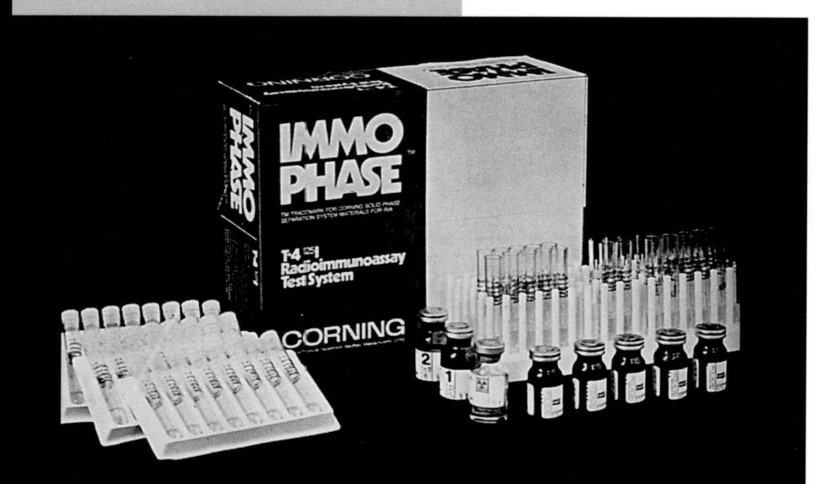

A more modest and ultimately much more successful venture in medical diagnostics was Corning's radioimmunoassay test kits. Developed by biologist Howard Weetall, the technology relied on the tendency of microscopic quantities of antigens in blood to bond to glass surfaces.

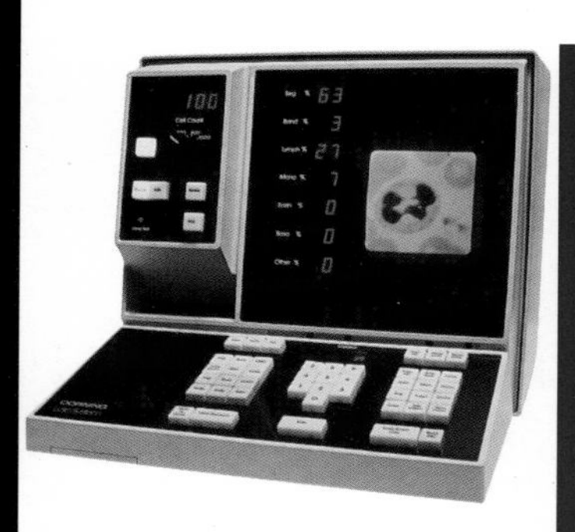

The most ambitious venture in new equipment was the Leukocyte Automatic Recognition Computer, a computer-based system to count white blood cells. Delivered late and well over budget, LARC failed in the marketplace and doomed Corning's plans to build electronic systems for its customers.

Corning took a small equity stake in MetPath, a fast-growing blood testing laboratory in Teeterboro, New Jersey, in 1973, then acquired it outright in 1982. MetPath served as the cornerstone of an aggressive strategy to build a nationwide clinical testing services company through acquisitions.

From clinical testing, Corning branched into pharmaceutical testing and environmental testing and analysis. Enseco, an environmental firm, arrived via acquisition in 1989. Several years later, under the leadership of Jim Kaiser, Enseco formed a joint venture with International Technology Inc. called Quanterra.

As Corning retreated from its diversified ventures, it also pulled back from a long-standing effort to market its glass tubing and engineering services to process industries. Pictured here: Pyrex tubing carry three different types of wine at the Taylor winery in Hammondsport, New York. In 1994, Corning Process Systems was sold in a management buyout.

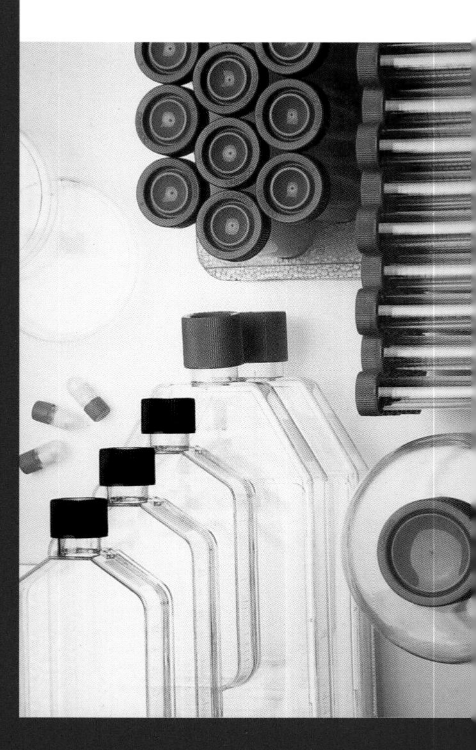

One venture that remains from the acquisitions of the 1990s is CoStar, a Massachusetts-based maker of plastic labware. CoStar complements and extends Corning's traditional business in laboratory glassware.

When Jamie Houghton succeeded his brother as chairman and CEO in 1983, he revamped top-level decision making. Rather than appoint a new president and chief operating officer, he formed a six-member committee to guide strategy and operations while also emphasizing teamwork.

Known formally as the Management Committee, the group was better known as the "Six Pack." Pictured with Houghton (center) are (clockwise, from lower left) Van Campbell, Dick Dulude, Marty Gibson, Bill Hudson, and Tom MacAvoy.

Houghton became an ardent champion of total quality management. In 1984, Corning established the Quality Council to oversee a major corporate initiative. It also set up the Quality Institute to provide training to every employee. The first class at the Institute included the company's senior management.

In the mid-1980s, the "Quapple" became a ubiquitous symbol of the company's emphasis on total quality.

In 1979, Corning helped lure the Ladies Professional Golf Association to an annual tournament each spring at Corning Country Club. Over the years the tournament raised millions for local hospitals and charities.

(far right) 1981 tournament winner, Kathy Hite

Named after former chairman Bill Decker, Corning's engineering building opened in 1980. The architects matched form with the way engineers work, creating open spaces for spontaneous meetings, numerous conference areas, and walls covered with white boards for sketching ideas and calculations.

Opened in June 1980, the curvilinear gallery at the Corning Museum of Glass exhibited nearly 20,000 pieces in historical sequence.

"The new building really resembles nothing so much as molten glass fresh from the firing tank and ready to accept any form that is imposed on it by its master craftsmen," wrote an admiring reviewer for *Smithsonian* magazine.

An Age of Communications

Since 1990

Twice before in its history—for the lighting and television industries—Corning had engineered glass materials and devised new production processes that contributed to revolutionary changes in industry and society. In the late 20th century, Corning did it again, through the development of optical waveguides—pure glass fibers as a nearly ideal medium for communications. This new technology made its first impact in long-distance telephone service, but it soon spread to other parts of the telecommunications network, cable TV, and the Internet. Along with the exciting new field of photonics—in which Corning also pioneered significant innovations—the technology promises in the 21st century to revolutionize not only information transport (communications) but also information processing (computing). Experts forecast that within a few years "all-optical computers" will operate at light speed, thousands of times faster than today's fastest supercomputers. As Corning marks 150 years of making glass, then, it is anything but an old company, and glass remains a remarkably versatile material in the "new economy" of postindustrial society.

Corning began work on glass fibers for communications in the late 1960s, as a result of contacts with laboratories at the British Post Office (now part of British Telecom). Three Corning researchers—physicists Robert Maurer and Donald Keck and chemist Peter Schultz—formed a team to pursue the possibility. A veteran research manager, Maurer had experience with lasers (a technology less than a decade old), as well as fused-silica glass in delay lines. Keck was an expert on measurement of optical transmission. Schultz had recently worked on making the purest form of glass through vapor deposition—a technology patented by Corning's Frank Hyde in the 1930s. The research team entered a high-stakes race to develop a feasible optical waveguide—as measured by a loss in transmission of less than 20 decibels per kilometer (db/km)—in competition with AT&T, ITT, and other telecommunications giants. There were many daunting technical challenges, from making glass pure enough, to designing the fiber to confine the light, to manufacturing fiber to meet performance objectives, including physical strength and durability.

The breakthrough came late on a Friday afternoon in August 1970. The last to leave the lab for the weekend, Keck lined up a laser at one end of the latest one-kilometer batch of experimental fiber for one final test. He crossed the lab to inspect the other end of the fiber, where a blast of bright light hit him in the eye. Subsequent measurement showed that the fiber produced a loss of only 16 db/km, well beyond the standard of feasibility. "Eureka," exclaimed Keck.

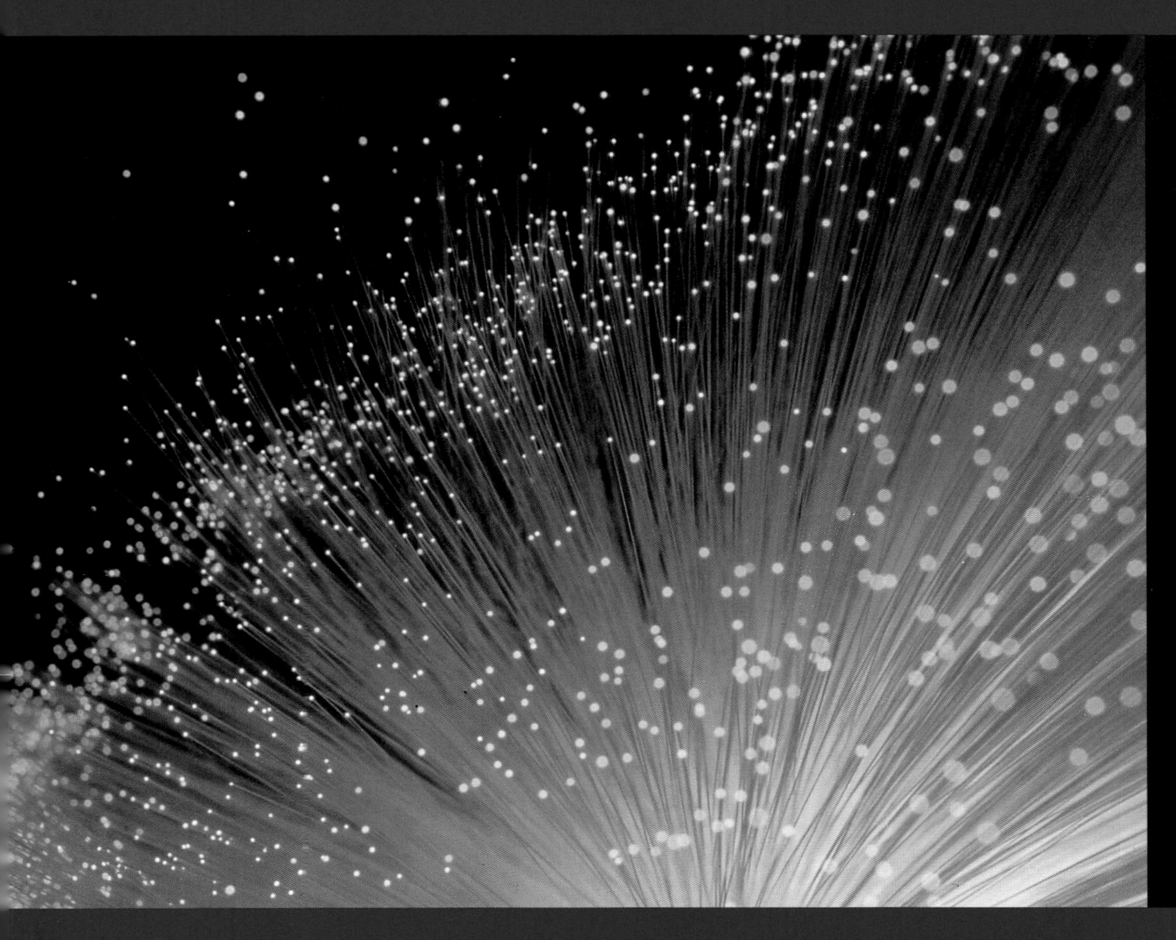

A new age of optical communications was soon to commence, but not before Corning rose to meet many more technical and commercial challenges. The scale and complexity of these led the company on two separate occasions to consider abandoning development in favor of licensing its patents to the major telecommunications companies. The first, in the early 1970s, came from a sense that Corning lacked the financial clout to develop the technology in the face of huge, endowed rivals like AT&T. Corning escaped this crisis by a clever development strategy that lined up partnerships with leading telecommunications companies outside of the United States, including BICC in the United Kingdom and Siemens in Germany. The second time Corning almost pulled the plug occurred during the corporate financial crisis of the mid-1970s. This time the faith of top management, especially Amo Houghton and R&D head Bill Armistead, that the company would make its future with fiber optics, remained unshakable and development continued.

During the 1970s and early 1980s, Corning researchers and engineers raced to develop better fibers and better ways of making them, while lining up new customers and anticipating advances in lasers and other related technologies. Development partnerships with BICC in the United Kingdom and Siemens in Germany blossomed into joint ventures to manufacture optical fiber. Corning and Siemens formed a second joint venture, Siecor Corp., to bind optical fibers into telecommunications cables. In 1980, Siecor acquired an independent cable company in Hickory, North Carolina, and moved its headquarters there. Meanwhile, under the leadership of Dave Duke, fresh off his development experience with Celcor, Corning accelerated fiber making through several generations of technology and moved operations from the labs and pilot plant near Corning to a revamped electronics factory in Wilmington, North Carolina. Along the way the company took many calculated risks by pushing exceedingly ambitious performance goals and incurring heavy expenditures by adding capacity well ahead of demand. The company also defended its patents vigorously, winning notable settlements with ITT, Sumitomo, and other competitors. And throughout the period Corning maintained its technological lead.

In 1982, Corning benefited from a major stroke of luck. The U.S. government settled an antitrust suit against AT&T under terms that permitted open competition in long-distance telecommunications. In short order, Corning and Siecor signed contracts with MCI and U.S. Sprint to supply many thousands of miles of fiber optic cable as the spines of new, nationwide telecommunications networks. Not long after, big telecommunications companies in Europe and Japan began placing large orders, and Corning was repeatedly challenged to keep pace with demand.

By 1990, Corning had established a secure and fast-growing position in optical communications on its own, as well as through Siecor. Corning was widely recognized as a technological powerhouse, and under the leadership of Jamie Houghton, the company as a whole attracted admiration for its commitments to technology, quality, and diversity, as well as its impressive financial performance. In 1994 the company was awarded the prestigious National Medal of Technology for its contributions to industry and society. A year later, its Telecommunications Products Division joined elite company as a winner of the Malcolm Baldrige National Quality Award.

In the 1990s, Corning extended its lead in communications through constant improvement of fibers, developing new products, and expanding into new markets. Several factors drove this rapid growth: vastly increased data traffic on the Internet and local area networks; the insatiable demand for high bandwidth communications to offices and residences; fierce competition among providers of telecommunications services, which became manifest in the push for constant improvement in telephone service; and the construction of major telecommunications networks in the developing economies, especially in Asia. Corning introduced new fiber designs optimized for specific uses, such as data transmission, or particular environments, such as underwater cable. To meet soaring demand, the company expanded its factory in Wilmington several times and built a second fiber plant in Concord, North Carolina. Corning also developed photonic components such as couplers, splitters, and fiber gain modules (amplifiers) to facilitate fiber optic communications. In 1998, the company opened a new facility dedicated to production of photonic components in Erwin, New York. Two years later it expanded the plant and opened two additional facilities in Benninton, Pennsylvania, and East Henrietta, New York to meet demand.

Under the leadership of Roger Ackerman, chairman and CEO after 1996, Corning surged to worldwide leadership in fiber optic communications through a series of major acquisitions. In 1998 Corning purchased its partner BICC's stake in Optical Fibres, Ltd., the joint venture fiber production facility in the United Kingdom. Corning followed the next year by purchasing Siemens's interest in a fiber joint venture in Germany and in Siecor Corp., the cable manufacturing company in the United States. These moves established Corning as the leading producer of fiber in North America and Europe and a major force in fiber optic cables.

In 1999-2000, Corning completed several more acquisitions to extend its product lines and bolster its competitive position. Merger with Oak Industries added diverse holdings, including Lasertron, a pioneering developer of semiconductor lasers. The purchase of Honeywell's Optical Polymer Group brought new capabilities in polymer-based photonic components such as switches. The arrival of NetOptix Corporation supplemented Corning's capabilities with expertise in thin film filters used in managing optical communications traffic. The stock market gave a resounding endorsement to these moves, driving Corning's share price to all-time record highs.

And so, 150 years after it all started, Corning's current health and future prospects seem brighter than ever. As symbols of the commitment of the company to innovation, Corning recently increased the level of its R&D spending dramatically, doubling the capacity of its complex at Sullivan Park and augmenting R&D facilities elsewhere in the United States, Europe, and Asia. With leading worldwide positions in optical communications, environmental, display, and specialty materials, the company seems poised to prosper in the new global, networked economy.

In the 1990s, Corning developed a fast-selling line of "photonic" devices to redirect and amplify light pulses. The components pictured here — optical filters, couplers, isolators, and lasers — are used in optical amplifiers for optical networks.

Although Corning had experience in making optical fibers, the intensity of its interest picked up after scientist Bill Shaver (pictured here addressing his colleagues) met with officials in British Telecom, who wanted fiber optic cable for videophones.

In 1970, Corning established the feasibility of glass fibers as optical waveguides. The team responsible for the initial development of waveguides included Donald Keck, Robert Maurer, and Peter Schultz.

Maurer led the project and contributed his deep knowledge of lasers; glass chemist Schultz developed the high-purity glasses for the fibers; and physicist Keck developed the measurements that enabled Corning to benchmark its progress.

To gain an edge in a fast-moving marketplace, Corning decided to pursue an untried, but potentially more efficient, way to make the extraordinarily pure glass needed for waveguides. Here Schultz monitors the outside vapor deposition process that ultimately enabled Corning to drive down fiber prices.

In a scene resembling the successful test on a fateful Friday afternoon in 1970, Keck (background) readies a one-kilometer sample of fiber to measure attenuation (light loss) from one end to the other.

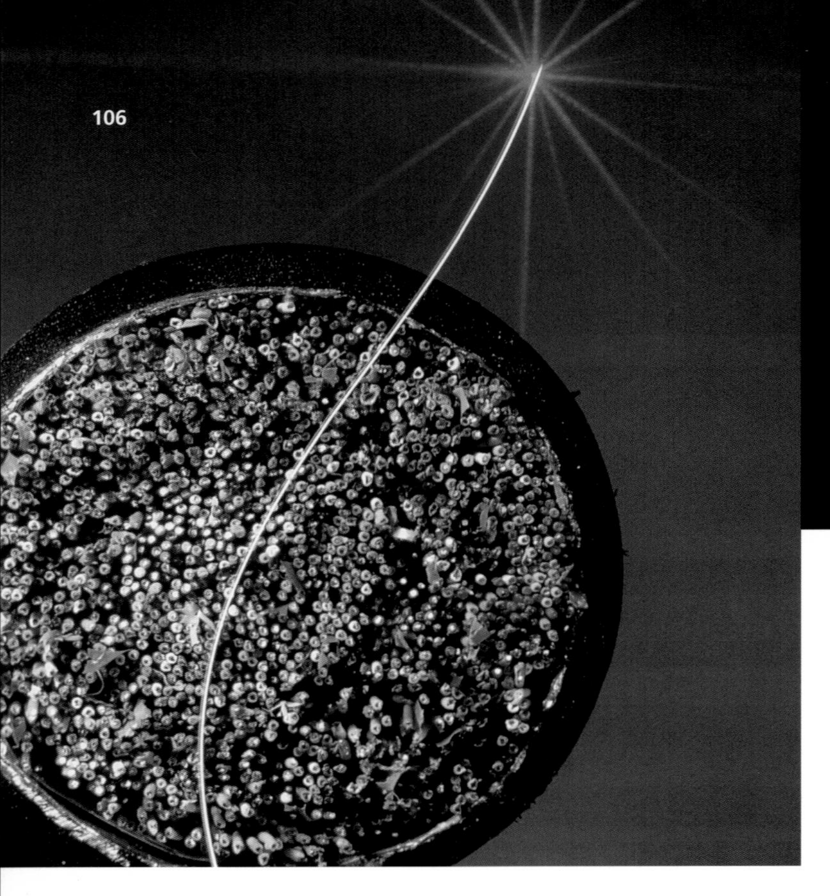

The capacity advantage of fiber over copper wire proved overwhelming and more than made up for a sizable difference in cost.

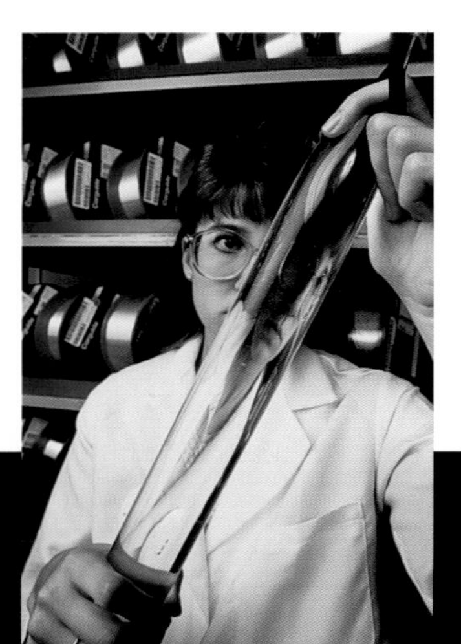

The process of drawing fiber begins with a glass "cane" such as this engineer is holding. Several kilometers of fiber can be drawn from a single cane.

In Corning's Wilmington, North Carolina factory, fiber is drawn using a downdraw process. As it cools, a protective coating is applied before it is wound onto spools in a continuous process.

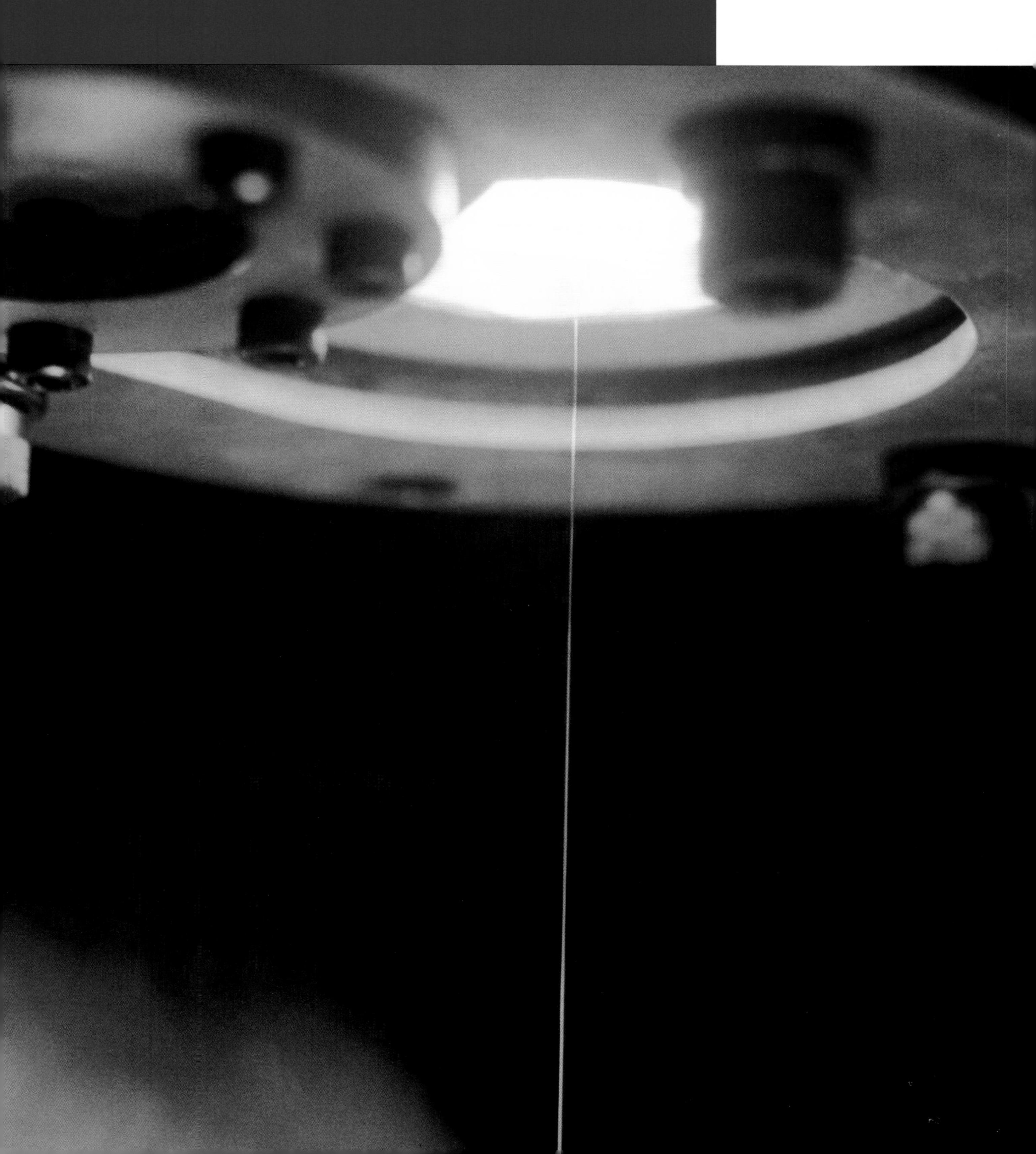

(right) State-of the-art technology at the new headquarters complex includes Corning optical fibers. Here workers install fiber optic cable in the building. Visible in the background is the Centerway bridge.

Corning and Siecor, its joint venture with Siemens GmbH, produced experimental batches of fiber optic cable in the late 1970s for test applications. By the end of the decade, Corning and Siecor had placed their bets in North Carolina, building a fiber plant in Wilmington and acquiring an established cable manufacturer in Hickory.

After Siecor acquired Superior Cable Company of Hickory, North Carolina, in 1980, headquarters shifted to a brand-new office building, a fitting location for a company fast on its way to hundreds of millions of dollars in annual sales within five years.

In 1982 an antitrust consent decree opened long distance communications to competition—just in time for Corning and Siecor. Here installers from U. S. Sprint lay fiber optic cable as the backbone of a new nationwide long distance network.

SIECOR
SIECOR
SIECOR
SIECOR

Side-by-side with its newest business in communications products, Corning maintained its oldest traditions as a supplier of specialty glass. Pictured: engineers at work on a mirror blank for the 327-inch, 35-ton Subaru telescope. Corning delivered the blank on schedule in 1994.

In 1994 the U. S. Department of Commerce bestowed on Corning the National Medal of Technology for its contributions to industry and society.

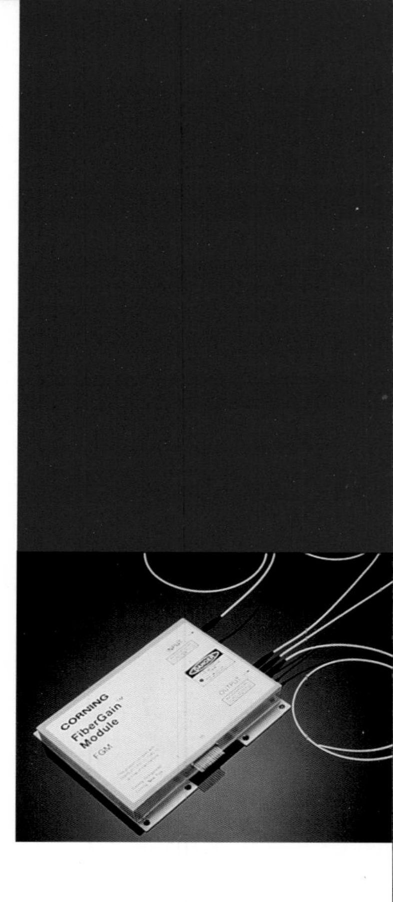

Jamie Houghton remained a tireless champion of total quality throughout his 13-year tenure as Corning's chief executive. In 1995, the year before he retired, Corning's Telecommunications Products Division won the prestigious Malcolm Baldrige National Quality Award — which is made of Steuben glass.

In 1996, a new management team took over at Corning, headed by Chairman and CEO Roger Ackerman. The team that assisted him included Vice Chairman Van Campbell, Norm Garrity, President of Corning Technologies, and John Loose, President of Corning Communications.

In 1999, Ackerman reassigned responsibilities when Campbell retired. Garrity became vice chairman and Loose was named president and chief operating officer. Two years later Loose succeeded Ackerman as CEO.

In 1999 Corning acquired Oak Industries, the corporate parent of Lasertron, a pioneer in semiconducting lasers that originate optical communications. The deal, and subsequent transactions in 1999 and 2000, positioned Corning to supply a broad range of optical communications products worldwide.

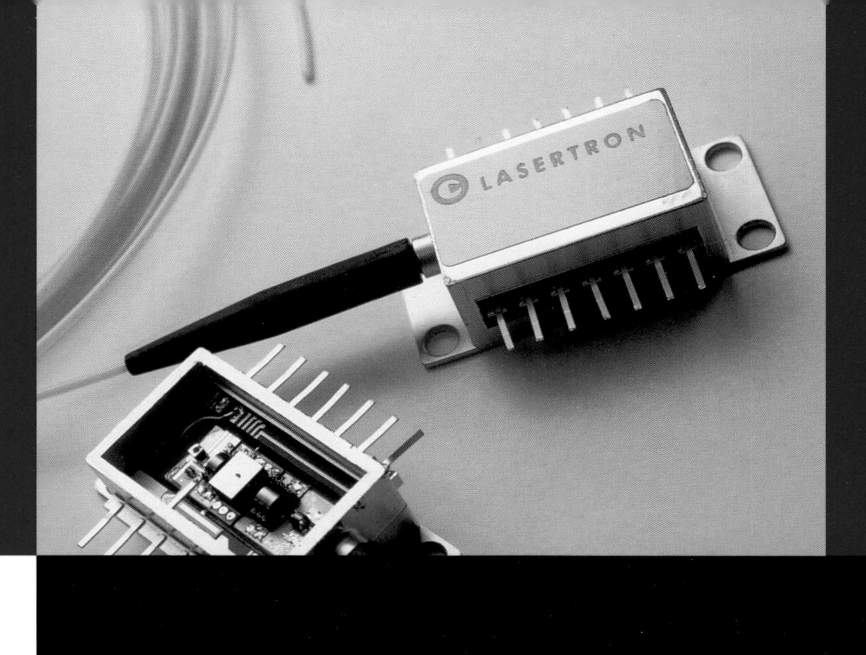

In the 1990s, Corning developed a fast-selling line of "photonic" devices to redirect and amplify light pulses. These splitters, couplers, and fiber gain modules stimulate fiber usage and position Corning for accelerated growth.

In the late 1990s, Corning once more reaffirmed the central role of science and technology in its business.

Forecasting a burst of growth in optical communications, specialty materials, and advanced life science products, the company doubled capacity at Sullivan Park, hired hundreds of new technical personnel, and expanded its network of R&D centers around the world.

Corning manufactures an array of photonic devices at a new facility in Erwin, New York, on the hillside below Sullivan Park. The facility features "clean rooms", advanced technology, and high performance work systems.

Corning's global network of R&D laboratories and centers includes this facility in St. Petersburg, Russia. The Russian lab houses leading scientists and engineers in optics and photonics.

Charles W. "Skip" Deneka Corning's chief technology officer between 1996 and 2001, played important roles in the development of Celcor and optical waveguides. In the late 1990s he presided over a pronounced increase in Corning's R&D investment

Corning moved into its headquarters complex in 1993, built on the site of the Main Plant and original executive offices of Corning Flint Glass Works.

The modular structure of the building (shown below under construction) accommodates the changing needs of the business, while atriums house glass sculptures by notable artists.

Marie McKee, president of The Corning Museum of Glass, and Jamie Houghton at the opening of the Museum's Innovation Center addition in June of 1999.

The Corning Museum of Glass Innovation Center features exhibits illustrating fundamental innovations derived from glass.

The Innovation Center was planned as a part of a multiyear expansion and renovation of the museum that culminated in its 50th anniversary in 2001.

Amid the astonishing changes of recent years, Corning remains close to its roots. This statue of a gaffer sits below the thermometer tube tower refurbished in 1999 as a continuing symbol of the company's presence in its hometown community.

Index

Acknowledgements

This book is one of three publications sponsored by Corning Incorporated in observance of the 150th anniversary of its first ventures in glass making. As such, it is a companion to two other books produced by The Winthrop Group, Inc.: Davis Dyer and Daniel Gross, *The Generations of Corning: The Life and Times of a Global Corporation*, and Margaret B.W. Graham and Alec T. Shuldiner, *Corning and the Craft of Innovation*, both books published by Oxford University Press in 2001, and it draws on the same basic research.

The author wishes to thank Marie McKee, senior vice president, Corning Incorporated, for serving as champion of the 150th Celebrations, of which this book is a key element. He would also like to thank the members of the History 150 Steering Committee at Corning Incorporated for their assistance with this project: Peter Bridenbaugh, W. Bernard Carlson, Rob Cassetti, Cindy Demers, Gus Filbert, Jack Holliday, Jamie Houghton, Eve Menger, Al Michaelsen, Meleny Peacock, and Stuart K. Sammis. Bernie Carlson, Meg Graham, and Stuart Sammis constituted a smaller committee to help develop the concept and contents of this work.

Kristine Gable and Gerry Orr performed exceptional service as photo researchers, poring over thousands of photographs and illustrations in company and community archives and helping to select the best for inclusion here. Michelle Cotton of Corning's Department of Archives and Records Management patiently and professionally assisted the research. Kris and Meg Graham assisted in preparing captions, fact checking, and obtaining releases and credits. Timothy Shaddock and Nancy Foster assisted with digitizing the images for layout. Judy Kohn, Lise Andersson and Mia Moran of Kohn Cruikshank designed the book and managed the production process. Chrisona Schmidt served as copy editor. Kathy Massimini compiled the index. Myrna Lopez of Harvard Translations coordinated translation into French, German, Japanese, and Spanish. We would also thank Dr. F. Okamoto, Akira Okada, Gerhard Konig, Maria José Mejia, Dr. Jacques Lemoine, and Helene Magne for their efforts in reviewing their respective language translations.

Dave Young and June Hyjek of Moore Corporation Ltd. managed the prepress and printing of this book in partnership with John Scalice of Applied Graphic Technologies and Lou Marcelino of Applied Printing Technologies. File composition and photo retouching performed by Rob Conte, Rick Carney, and Paul Morgan of Applied Graphic Technologies.

Photographers:

The vast majority of illustrations used in this book are reproduced by courtesy of Corning Incorporated. We have sought to credit as many images originating from other sources as possible in the list below. The age and unknown circumstances of some items makes tracing their provenance impossible today.

Bachrach photo: p 28 bottom right

Robert Barker: p 78, p 79 top, p 79 bottom, p 82-83, p 93, p 94 top right, p 95 right, p 96 bottom four images, p 106 top

Frank J. Borkowski: p 99, p 101, p 106 bottom right, p 112 top left, p 112 top right, p 112-113, p 114, p 115 top

Collection of The Corning Museum of Glass: p 6, p 12 top right, p 12 top left, p 117 top left, p 118

Courtesy of Corning-Painted Post Historical Society, p 10-11 top, p 13, p 13, p 25 top

© Scott Frances/Esto, p 117 top right

Mike Greenlar: p 106 bottom left

C. Huston: p 43

Courtesy of J. Franklin Hyde: p 56 top left

Chris Ibberson: p 60 top

Kellogg Studios: p 64, p 97

Courtesy of LPGA Corning Classic: p 98 top right

Photo provided by Lasertron: p 113 top

Courtesy of Littleton Family: p 42

Courtesy of Edward K. Lofberg: p 18-19

Courtesy of Market Street Restoration Agency: p 74-75, p 75 bottom (delete "right")

Forest McMullin: p 72 top

Robert Moore (both Steuben pieces): p 85 middle

Hank Morgan: p 70 top

Steve Myers: p 60 middle right, p 71 top, p 73 bottom, p 79 middle left, p 79 middle, second from left, p 79 middle right, p 111 top

NASA Photo: #84-HC-6, p 91 top right

Michael Orr Associates: p 44 middle middle

Frank Petronio: p 29 top

Courtesy of G. Clint Shay: p 72 middle left

Photo provided by Siecor: p. 108 bottom right

Ayres A. Stevens: p 50-51, p 51 top

© Jamey Stillings: p 96 top

Charles Swain Photography: p 79 middle, second from right, p 117 bottom

Underwood and Underwood: p. 52

Photo provided by USPL: p 73 top

Photo provided by U.S. Sprint: p 108 bottom

Wide World Photo: #R59118, p 90-91

© Tom Watson: p 109, p 116-117

Weymouth Design, Inc.: p 115 bottom

Ed Wheeler: p 68 top left, p 103, p 112 bottom

Nicholay Zurek: p 87

All other photographs: Courtesy of Corning Incorporated, Corporate Archives.